CAROLS FOR TODAY

WORDS EDITION

JUBILATE HYMNS

EDITOR: MICHAEL PERRY

MUSIC EDITOR: DAVID ILIFF

GU00383902

Hodder & Stoughton

LONDON SYDNEY AUCKLAND TORONTO

Copyright Information

Full copyright details are available in the Music edition of *Carols For Today*. Every effort has been made to trace copyright-holders and to obtain permission; the publishers would welcome details of any error or omission, and will incorporate corrections in future reprints.

British Library Cataloguing in Publication Data

Carols for today: Jubilate Hymns — words edition
1. Carols, English — texts
I. Perry, Michael
783.6'2'0942   PR1195.C2

ISBN 0-340-41680-7

Carols For Today: full music, edited by Michael Perry and David Iliff for Jubilate Hymns, is published by Hodder & Stoughton and available in boards and limp editions.

Carols For Today: record, featuring the choir of Canterbury Cathedral directed by Dr. Allan Wicks, producer Barry Rose, is available in LP, CD and Stereo Cassette formats on the Conifer label from record shops.

Also by Jubilate Hymns from Hodder & Stoughton: *Hymns for Today's Church* (*Full Music, Melody,* and *Words editions*); *Church Family Worship* (*Boards, Limp,* and *Music editions*).

CAROLS

1 From the Latin, J M Neale and others
© in this version Jubilate Hymns †
Tune: Veni Emmanuel

1 O come, O come, Emmanuel
and ransom captive Israel
who mourns in lonely exile here
until the Son of God draws near:
Rejoice, rejoice!
Emmanuel shall come to you, O Israel.

2 O come, true Branch of Jesse, free
your children from this tyranny;
from depths of hell your people save
to rise victorious from the grave:
Rejoice, rejoice . . .

3 O come, bright Daybreak,
    come and cheer
our spirits by your advent here;
dispel the long night's lingering gloom
and pierce the shadows of the tomb:
Rejoice, rejoice . . .

4 O come, strong Key of David, come
and open wide our heavenly home;
make safe the way that leads on high,
and close the path to misery:
Rejoice, rejoice . . .

5 O come, O come, great Lord of might
who long ago on Sinai's height
gave all your tribes the ancient law,
in cloud and majesty and awe!
Rejoice, rejoice . . .

2 C Wesley, © in this version Jubilate Hymns †
Tune: Cross of Jesus

1 Come, O long-expected Jesus,
born to set your people free!
from our fears and sins release us,
Christ in whom our rest shall be.

2 Israel's strength and consolation,
born salvation to impart;
dear desire of every nation,
joy of every longing heart:

3 Born your people to deliver,
born a child and yet a king;
born to reign in us for ever,
now your gracious kingdom bring:

4 By your own eternal Spirit
rule in all our hearts alone;
by your all-sufficient merit
raise us to your glorious throne.

3 From the Latin, © Michael Perry †
Tune: Conditor alme siderum (or LM)
Shorter version: omit verses 4 and 5

1 Creator of the stars of light,
our Lord of mercy and of might,
the Christ, redeemer of us all:
O hear your people when they call.

2 Through you, the saviour crucified,
the guilty age of death has died;
you took our frail humanity
and gave the world its remedy.

3 And in the evening of our day
you rose to drive the shades away;
from Mary's honoured virgin womb
you came, to take your people home.

4 The sun returning to the west,
the moon in pallid splendour dressed,
the glittering stars that pierce the skies,
obedient, keep their boundaries.

5 The unseen worlds below, above,
at your supreme direction move;
soon every creature of your hand
shall bow to your divine command.

6 We plead with you, our judge and Lord,
to come according to your word;
and in that hour of destiny
to save us from the enemy.

7 Now to the Father, with the Son
and Holy Spirit, Three-in-One;
to God whom heaven and earth adore
be praise and glory evermore! Amen.

4 F. L. Hosmer © in this version Word & Music †
Tune: Irish

1 Your kingdom come! On bended knee
    through passing years we pray:
all faithful people long to see
    on earth that kingdom's day.

2 The hours of waiting through the night
    no less to God belong;
the stars declare the eternal right
    and shame the creature's wrong.

3 And there already in the skies
    the dawn's first rays appear —
you prophets of our God, arise,
    proclaim the day is near:

4 The day in whose clear shining light
    the Lord shall stand revealed,
and every wrong be turned to right,
    and every hurt be healed:

5 When justice joined with truth and peace
    make straight the Saviour's road —
the day of perfect righteousness,
    the promised day of God!

5 From the Latin, © Michael Perry †
Tune: Splendour

1 O come, our world's Redeemer, come!
Let every age astonished be
that God should grace the Virgin's womb
and take our frail humanity.

2 For not by mortal will or power,
but by the Holy Spirit's breath
the seed of heaven comes to flower,
the Word made flesh is found on earth.

3 He comes, for whom creation yearns,
to face the realms of death alone;
and to the Father he returns
to gain a kingdom and a throne.

4 He comes to triumph over wrong
and bring us captive back to heaven;
for in our weakness he is strong,
and for his sake we are forgiven.

5 O come, our world's Redeemer, come!
Your manger shines upon our night —
so let the voice of doubt be dumb,
for none shall quench this glorious light!

6 G Weissel and C Winkworth
© in this version Word & Music †
Tune: Gonfalon Royal

1 Lift up your heads, you mighty gates;
behold, the Lord of glory waits,
the King of kings is drawing near,
the saviour of the world he here!

2 O blessed the land, the city blessed
where Christ the ruler is confessed;
O happy hearts and happy homes
to whom this King in triumph comes!

3 Redeemer, come! — we open wide
our hearts to you this Advent-tide:
so let your Spirit guide us on
until the glorious hope is won! Amen.

OR, AT CHRISTMAS
3 Redeemer, come! — we open wide
our hearts to you this Christmastide:
so let your Spirit guide us on
until the glorious hope is won! Amen.

7 From Psalms 85 and 86, J Milton
© in this version Word & Music †
Tune: St Stephen

1 The Lord will come and not be slow,
his footsteps cannot err;
before him righteousness shall go,
his royal harbinger.

2 Truth from the earth, like to a flower,
shall bud and blossom then;
and justice shall in heavenly shower
come down to us again.

3 Rise, God, and judge the earth in might,
its wicked ways redress;
for you are he who shall by right
the nations all possess!

4 The nations all, whom you have made,
shall all your works acclaim,
and come to bow before you, Lord,
and glorify your name.

5 For great you are, and wonders great
by your strong hand are done;
in high and everlasting state
you reign as God alone.

8 From Isaiah 40, © David Mowbray†
Tune: St Bernard

1 Take God's good news
      to saddened hearts:
an end to tears there'll be —
the glory of the Lord shall shine,
and all the world shall see!

2 The grass shall fade, the flowers shall fall —
no earthly friend is sure;
but God has spoken, and his word
shall stand for evermore.

3 Good news for you, Jerusalem!
good news for lands afar —
the Lord shall come, his arm shall rule
and war shall be no more.

4 The patient Shepherd feeds his flock,
and gathers every lamb;
he shields them all, the Mighty One,
and keeps his sheep from harm.

5 How blessed the heralds of good news
who spread God's word of peace;
who sing aloud the Saviour's name,
'The Lord our Righteousness':

6 From mountain-top let voices ring,
'In Christ, our God has come —
to share our life, to bear our grief,
to bring us safely home!'

9 From Luke 12, P Doddridge
© in this version Word & Music †
Tune: Narenza

1 You servants of the Lord
who for his coming wait:
observe with care his heavenly word —
be watchful at his gate.

2 Let all your lamps be bright
and guard the living flame;
be ready always in his sight,
for awesome is his name.

3 Await your Lord's command —
the bridegroom shall appear:
for his returning is at hand,
and while we speak he's near.

4 O happy servants they
who wide awake are found
to greet their master on that day,
and be with honour crowned!

5 Christ shall the banquet spread
with his own royal hand,
and raise each faithful servant's head
amid the angelic band.

10 After P Nicolai, © Christopher Idle †
Tune: Sleepers wake

1 Wake, O wake, and sleep no longer,
for he who calls you is no stranger:
awake, God's own Jerusalem!
Hear the midnight bells are chiming
the signal for his royal coming:
let voice to voice announce his name!
We feel his footstep near,
the Bridegroom at the door —
Alleluia!
The lamps will shine
with light divine
as Christ the saviour comes to reign.

2 Zion hears the sound of singing;
her heart is thrilled with sudden longing:
she stirs, and wakes, and stands prepared.
Christ her friend, and lord, and lover,
her star and sun and strong redeemer —
at last his mighty voice is heard.
The Son of God has come
to make with us his home:
sing Hosanna!
The fight is won,
the feast begun;
we fix our eyes on Christ alone.

3 Glory, glory, sing the angels,
while music sounds
from strings and cymbals:
all humankind, with songs arise!
Twelve the gates into the city,
each one a pearl of shining beauty;
the streets of gold ring out with praise.
All creatures round the throne
adore the holy One
with rejoicing:
Amen be sung
by every tongue
to crown their welcome to the King.

11 After J Cennick; C Wesley and M Madan
Tune: Helmsley

1 Lo, he comes with clouds descending,
once for favoured sinners slain;
thousand thousand saints attending
swell the triumph of his train:
Alleluia, alleluia, alleluia!
God appears, on earth to reign.

2 Every eye shall now behold him
robed in dreadful majesty;
those who set at naught and sold him,
pierced and nailed him to the tree,
deeply wailing . . .
shall the true Messiah see.

3 The dear tokens of his passion
still his dazzling body bears,
cause of endless exultation
to his ransomed worshippers:
with what rapture . . .
gaze we on those glorious scars!

4 Yea, Amen, let all adore thee,
high on thine eternal throne;
Saviour, take the power and glory,
claim the kingdom for thine own:
Alleluia . . .
everlasting God, come down!

12 From the Latin, E Caswall
Tune: Merton

1 Hark! a trumpet call is sounding,
'Christ is near,' it seems to say:
'Cast away the dreams of darkness,
children of the dawning day!'

2 Wakened by the solemn warning,
let the earth-bound soul arise;
Christ, her sun, all harm dispelling,
shines upon the morning skies.

3 See! the Lamb, so long expected,
comes with pardon down from heaven;
let us haste, with tears of sorrow,
one and all to be forgiven:

4 That, when next he comes in glory
and the world is wrapped in fear,
with his mercy he may shield us,
and with words of love draw near.

5 Honour, glory, might and blessing
to the Father, and the Son,
with the everlasting Spirit,
while eternal ages run!

13 E Farjeon, © Oxford University Press
Tune: Besançon Carol

1 People, look east, the time is near
of the crowning of the year;
make your house fair as you are able,
trim the hearth and set the table.
People, look east, and sing today —
Love the Guest is on the way.

2 Furrows, be glad though earth is bare —
one more seed is planted there;
gird up your strength the seed to nourish,
that in time the flower may flourish.
People, look east, and sing today —
Love, the Rose, is on the way.

3 Stars, keep the watch when night is dim —
one more light the bowl shall brim,
shining beyond the frosty weather,
bright as sun and moon together.
   People, look east, and sing today —
   Love the Star is on the way.

4 Angels, announce to man and beast:
he is coming from the east;
set every peak and valley humming
with the word: the Lord is coming!
   People, look east, and sing today —
   Love, the Lord, is on the way.

14 From Isaiah 61, P Doddridge
Tune: Bristol

1 Hark the glad sound! — the Saviour comes,
the Saviour promised long;
let every heart prepare a throne
and every voice a song.

2 He comes the prisoners to release
in Satan's bondage held;
the gates of brass before him burst,
the iron fetters yield.

3 He comes the broken heart to bind,
the wounded soul to cure;
and with the treasures of his grace
to enrich the humble poor.

4 Our glad hosannas, Prince of peace,
your welcome shall proclaim;
and heaven's eternal arches ring
with your belovèd name.

15 Margaret Clarkson, © Hope Publishing Co. Inc.
Tune: Little Cornard

1 Jesus the saviour comes!
Greet him with joyful song,
prince of the heavenly throne,
promised to earth so long:
he comes to fight our mortal foe
and carry all our sin and woe.

2 Jesus the saviour comes!
Lord over life and death;
sin and destruction die,
felled by his holy breath:
triumphant from the cross and grave
he comes to heal and bless and save.

3 Jesus the saviour comes!
sovereign and Lord of all;
kingdoms, dominions, powers —
all at his feet must fall:
he comes to banish death and sin
and bring his great salvation in.

4 Lord of the Christmas crib,
Lord of the cross of shame,
humbly we worship you,
proudly we take your name:

be all our joy till advent drums
and trumpets cry, 'The saviour comes!'

5 Then with your ransomed hosts,
faultless before your face,
sons of the living God,
born of redeeming grace,
your love we'll sing,
   your power we'll praise:
your name adore through endless days!

16 After C Coffin, © Michael Perry †
Tune: St Thomas

1 We hail the approaching God,
who quickly comes from heaven,
and celebrate with festive songs
such love so freely given.

2 Within a virgin's womb
he hides his liberty;
the immortal Lord becomes a slave
to set his people free.

3 O run to greet your king
who stands on Zion's hill:
to all who hear his word of peace,
his arms are stretched out still.

4 Soon, shining in the cloud,
the Lord will come again
and take his Body to the skies
to live and love and reign.

5 Then night and death shall yield,
and sin be done away;
then Adam shall be made anew
on that tremendous day.

6 To Father, Spirit, Son,
the God whom we adore,
be highest praise and honour now,
and glory evermore!

17 From Luke 2 — *The Song of Simeon/*
Nunc Dimittis, © Michael Perry †
Tune: Halton Holgate

1 Jesus, hope of every nation,
light of heaven upon our way;
promise of the world's salvation,
spring of life's eternal day!

2 Saints by faith on God depending
wait to see Messiah born;
sin's oppressive night is ending
in the glory of the dawn.

3 Look, he comes! — the long-awaited
Christ, redeemer, living Word;
hope and faith are vindicated
as with joy we greet the Lord.

4 Glory in the highest heaven
to the Father, Spirit, Son;
and on earth let praise be given
to our God, the Three-in-One!

18 I Watts
Tune: Antioch

1 Joy to the world — the Lord has come:
let earth receive her king,
let every heart prepare him room
   and heaven and nature sing,
   and heaven and nature sing,
   and heaven, and heaven and nature sing!

2 Joy to the earth — the saviour reigns:
let songs be heard on high,
while fields and streams
      and hills and plains
   repeat the sounding joy,
   repeat the sounding joy,
   repeat, repeat the sounding joy.

3 He rules the world with truth and grace,
and makes the nations prove
the glories of his righteousness,
   the wonders of his love,
   the wonders of his love,
   the wonders, wonders of his love.

19 Traditional, collected by E M Leather &
R Vaughan Williams
© Stainer & Bell Ltd, in this version Word & Music †
Tune: The Truth from above

1 Christ is the Truth sent from above,
the Truth of God, the God of love:
therefore don't turn him from your door,
but hear him all, both rich and poor.

2 Though God had given us all things good,
yet sin we did and sin we would;
though we were heirs to death and hell,
God sent his Son with us to dwell.

3 For at this season of the year
our blessed redeemer did appear;
he came to serve and came to teach,
and many thousands heard him preach.

4 Thus he in love to us behaved,
and showed us how we must be saved;
to free us from our mortal pain,
he lived and died and rose again.

20 From Isaiah 9, J Morison
© in this version Jubilate Hymns †
Tune: Dundee

1 The people who in darkness walked
have seen a glorious light:
that light shines out on those who lived
in shadows of the night.

2 To greet you, Sun of righteousness,
the gathering nations come;
rejoicing as when reapers bring
their harvest treasures home.

3 For now to us a child is born,
to us a son is given;
and on his shoulder ever rests
all power in earth and heaven.

4 His name shall be the prince of peace,
eternally adored;
most wonderful of counsellors,
the great and mighty Lord.

5 His peace and righteous government
shall over all extend;
on judgement and on justice based,
his reign shall never end.

21/22 From Isaiah 9 etc, © Timothy Dudley-Smith
Tunes: Saigon, Sandys

1 The darkness turns to dawn,
the dayspring shines from heaven;
for unto us a child is born,
to us a Son is given.

2 The Son of God most high,
before all else began,
a virgin's son behold him lie,
the new-born Son of Man.

3 God's Word of truth and grace
made flesh with us to dwell;
the brightness of the Father's face,
the child Emmanuel.

4 How rich his heavenly home!
How poor his human birth!
as mortal man he stoops to come,
the light and life of earth.

5 A servant's form, a slave,
the Lord consents to share;
our sin and shame, our cross and grave,
he bows himself to bear.

6 Obedient and alone
upon that cross to die,
and then to share the Father's throne
in majesty on high.

7 And still God sheds abroad
that love so strong to send
a saviour, who is Christ the Lord,
whose reign shall never end.

23 © Isobel Kiddle
Tune: Sibford Gower

1 Bow down, you stars and moon and sun!
the Source of all your light is come;
the fire that burns within his heart
is such that yours is but a part
   of his pure radiance.

2 You measured years and hours and days,
fill every moment with his praise:
for he who knows no time or space
confines himself within this place —
the eternal Word, made flesh.

3 Lift up your heads, you sons of earth!
your great Creator comes to birth;
and with a baby's lonely cry,
he prophesies his agony
to draw you to himself.

4 No thrilling music with its spell,
no artist's brush, or pen can tell
the yearning love, consuming care
that brings you to that manger bare —
our Lord, Emmanuel.

5 Lord Jesus, Saviour, mighty King,
our lives, our all, to you we bring;
for by that lowly path you trod,
you loved us back to you, our God —
to make us heirs of heaven!

24 O Goldschmidt after W Bartholomew
© collected 1964 Gamut Distribution
Tune: A tender shoot

1 A tender shoot has started
up from a root of grace,
as ancient seers imparted
from Jesse's holy race;
    it blooms without a blight,
    it blooms without a blight,
blooms in the cold bleak winter
turning our darkness into light.

2 This shoot, Isaiah taught us,
from Jesse's root should spring;
the virgin Mary brought us
the branch of whom we sing:
    our God of endless might,
    our God of endless might
gave her this child to save us,
thus turning darkness into light.

25 From the Latin, © Michael Perry †
Tune: Angelus ad virginem

1 Gabriel the angel came
to greet the virgin Mary:
'Peace!' he said, and called her name,
'For joyful news I carry:
the Lord of all from realms above
has looked upon your soul in love;
    you shall give birth
    to Christ on earth,
    the Saviour;
you bear the hope of grace —
the mark of heaven's favour,
and all shall see God's face.'

2 Mary asked, 'How can it be:
my love is given to no-one,
Joseph is betrothed to me —
can what is done be undone?'
'The Spirit comes — and this is how
God's power will be upon you now:
    Don't be afraid
    what God has said
    will cheer you —
the promise is not in vain —
all people shall revere you,
and virtue shall remain.'

3 Mary then with joy replied
'I serve the Lord of heaven:
God shall be my hope and guide
to him my heart is given
who lowly stoops to fill my cup
and raise his humble servant up.
    God's will this day
    I shall obey
    rejoicing:
then let the nations sing,
such love and mercy voicing,
and praise their Lord and king!'

26 After the traditional carol, © Michael Perry †
Tune: Sans Day Carol

1 When the angel came to Mary
he said, 'Be at peace,
for the Lord God shall be with you,
his love will not cease.'
    And Mary bore Jesus Christ,
    our saviour for to be;
    and the first and the last
    and the greatest is he, is he, is he;
    and the first and the last
    and the greatest is he.

2 When the angel came to Mary
he said, 'Do not fear,
for his power shall be upon you,
a child you will bear.'
    And Mary bore Jesus Christ . . .

3 When the angel came to Mary
he said, 'Hear his name,
for his title shall be Jesus
of kingly acclaim.'
    And Mary bore Jesus Christ . . .

4 When the angel came to Mary,
she said, 'Be it so:
for the Lord God is my master,
his will I must do.'
    And Mary bore Jesus Christ . . .

27 S Baring-Gould, © in this version Word & Music †
Tune: Gabriel's Message

1 The angel Gabriel from heaven came,
   his wings as drifted snow,
      his eyes as flame:
   'From God, all hail,' the angel said to Mary,
   'most highly favoured lady!'
   Gloria!

2 'Fear not, for you shall bear a holy child,
   by him shall man to God be reconciled,
   his name shall be Emmanuel,
      the long-foretold:
   most highly favoured lady!'
   Gloria!

3 Then gentle Mary humbly bowed
      her head:
   'To me be as it pleases God,' she said,
   'My soul shall praise and magnify
      his holy name.'
   Most highly favoured lady!
   Gloria!

4 'And so,' she said, 'how happy I shall be!
   All generations will remember me,
   for God has kept the promises to Israel.'
   Most highly favoured lady!
   Gloria!

5 Of her, Emmanuel — the Christ — was born
   in Bethlehem, upon that Christmas morn.
   And Christian folk throughout the world
      will ever say,
   'Most highly favoured lady!
   Gloria!'

28 From Luke 1, *The Song of Mary/Magnificat*
© Christopher Idle †
Tune: Andrew Mark

1 My soul proclaims
      the greatness of the Lord,
   and my spirit sings for joy
      to my saviour God!
   His lowly slave he looked upon in love:
   they will call me happy now,
   for mighty are the works he has done,
   and holy is his name!

2 In every age, for those who fear the Lord
   come his mercy,
      and the strength of his mighty arm:
   he routs the proud,
      throws monarchs off their thrones,
   while he lifts the lowly high,
   fills hungry souls with food,
   and the rich sends empty away.

3 To Israel his servant he brings help,
   and the promise to our fathers
      is now fulfilled:
   for Christ has come according to his word,
   and the mercy that he showed
      to Abraham is now
   for his children's children evermore.

29 From Luke 1 — *The Song of Mary/Magnificat*
© Michael Saward †
Tune: Bitterne (or LM)

1 Now sing, my soul, 'How great the Lord!' —
      rejoice, my spirit, in your God:
   my saviour who has looked on me,
      a humble servant in his sight.

2 For ever after, I'll be known
      as happiest of the human race;
   the mighty One has dealt with me,
      and holy, holy is his name.

3 Throughout all ages, those who fear
      his majesty, shall know his grace;
   his powerful works disclose his might,
      he routs the arrogant in heart.

4 From thrones great rulers have been torn,
      yet humble folk are raised on high;
   the hungry have been satisfied,
      the wealthy, he shall turn away.

5 To Israel, servant of the Lord,
      comes yet again the promised hope:
   in Abraham and all his line,
      God's mercy ever shall endure.

6 Give glory then to God above,
      give praise to Christ his only Son;
   give thanks for all the Spirit's power,
      both now and through eternity!

30 English traditional
© in this version Word & Music †
Tune: Cherry Tree Carol

1 As Joseph was awaking
   he heard an angel sing,
   'There shall be born to Mary
   on earth our heavenly King.'

2 And neither was he born
   in house nor yet in hall;
   nor in the place of paradise,
   but in an ox's stall.

3 And neither was he covered
   in finery so fair,
   but in such humble clothing
   as all the babies wear.

4 And neither was he cradled
   in silver nor in gold,
   but in a wooden manger
   to keep him from the cold.

5 As Joseph was awaking
   he heard an angel sing,
   'There shall be born to Mary
   on earth our heavenly King.'

31
English traditional
© in this version Word & Music †
Tune: Joseph

   As Joseph was awaking
   he heard an angel sing,
   'There shall be born to Mary
   on earth our heavenly King.'

1 And neither was he born
   in house nor yet in hall;
   nor in the place of paradise,
   but in an ox's stall.
      Nowell, nowell!
      As Joseph . . .

2 And neither was he covered
   in finery so fair,
   but in such humble clothing
   as all the babies wear.
      Nowell, nowell!
      As Joseph . . .

3 And neither was he cradled
   in silver nor in gold,
   but in a wooden manger
   to keep him from the cold.
      Nowell, nowell!

32
© Paul Wigmore †
Tune: Stranger in Bethlehem

1 To Bethlehem the strangers came
   from all the country round,
   and unaware that God was there
   they fell to sleeping sound:
      Stranger in Bethlehem
      to whom the angels sing;
      manger in Bethlehem,
      cradle for a king!

2 To Bethlehem the strangers came,
   sweet Mary and her man,
   no room to spare, no comfort where
   a holy life began:
      Stranger in Bethlehem . . .

3 To Bethlehem a Stranger came
   from far beyond the earth;
   he came to share his Father's care,
   to bring us second birth:
      Stranger in Bethlehem . . .

33
English traditional
© in this version Word & Music †
Tune: A virgin most pure

1 A virgin most holy — as prophets do tell —
   has brought forth a baby
      among us to dwell,
   to be our redeemer
      from death and from sin,
   which Adam's transgression
      had caught us all in.
   And therefore be merry —
      rejoice and be merry,
      make music and sing,
   for Jesus our saviour
      is born to be king!

2 At Bethlehem Judah, a city renowned,
   both Mary and Joseph — his parents —
      were found;
   they came to be counted,
      with other folk too,
   as Caesar Augustus had said
      they should do.
   And therefore . . .

3 But when they had entered the city so fair,
   they could not get shelter,
      for many were there;
   and Joseph and Mary,
      whose substance was small,
   could find at the inn there no lodging at all.
   And therefore . . .

4 Then were they obliged
      in a stable to sleep,
   where travellers
      horses and donkeys did keep;
   they had there poor comfort
      and slept on the hay,
   but Mary bore Jesus, our saviour, next day.
   And therefore . . .

34
© Paul Wigmore †
Tune: Besançon Carol

1 Mary, ride on to David's town,
   Bethlehem with glory crown;
   bear your child to bear our weeping,
   rock him waking, rock him sleeping.
      Alleluia! Sing this night:
      Christ is born, eternal light!

2 Shepherds, come see in David's town,
   shepherd of the world come down;
   see your saviour, see your healing,
   worship humbly, worship kneeling.
      Alleluia! Sing this night . . .

3 Angels, proclaim to David's town
   Jesus Christ of high renown!
   Son of Man and king of glory,
   here to tell salvation's story.
      Alleluia! Sing this night . . .

35 After E Flèchier, © Michael Perry †
Tune: Dans cette étable

1 Child in a stable:
  how lovely is this place
    where God is able
  to show such perfect grace!
  No princely babe that smiled
  or palace that beguiled,
  in history or fable,
  could ever match this Child
    within a stable.

2 God comes in weakness,
  and to our world for love
    descends with meekness
  from realms of light above.
  This Child shall heal our wrong,
  for sorrow give a song,
  and hope in place of bleakness;
  for nothing is so strong
    as God in weakness.

3 Now night is ended!
  the chasm that divides
    at last is mended,
  and God with us abides.
  For on this happy morn
  new glory wakes the dawn;
  the Sun is high ascended —
  to us a Child is born,
    and night is ended!

36 From *Advice to a prophet*, Richard Wilbur
© Faber and Faber Limited
Tune: Dayton

1 A stable lamp is lighted
  whose glow shall wake the sky;
  the stars shall bend their voices,
    and every stone shall cry,
  and straw like gold shall shine;
  a barn shall harbour heaven,
  a stall become a shrine.

2 This child through David's city
  shall ride in triumph by;
  the palm shall strew its branches,
    and every stone shall cry,
  though heavy, dull, and dumb,
  and lie within the roadway
  to pave his kingdom come.

3 Yet he shall be forsaken,
  and yielded up to die;
  the sky shall groan and darken,
    and every stone shall cry
  for stony hearts of men;
  God's blood upon the spearhead,
  God's love refused again.

4 But now, as at the ending,
  the low is lifted high;
  the stars shall bend their voices,
    and every stone shall cry

in praises of the Child
by whose descent among us
the worlds are reconciled.

37/38 R. Southwell
© in this version Word & Music †
Tunes: Newtown Linford, Peak Hill

1 Come, see a little tender babe,
  in freezing winter night,
  who in a manger trembling lies,
  a sad and sorry sight.

2 The inns are full, and none will give
  this little pilgrim bed,
  but forced is he among the beasts
  in crib to shroud his head.

3 Despise him not for lying there;
  first, what he is enquire:
  an orient pearl is often found
  in depths of dirty mire.

4 Judge not his crib, his wooden dish,
  nor beasts that by him feed;
  judge not his mother's poor attire,
  nor Joseph's manner heed.

5 This stable is a prince's court,
  this crib his chair of state;
  the beasts are part of all his pomp,
  the dish his royal plate.

6 The persons in that poor attire
  his royal liveries wear;
  the Prince himself
    has come from heaven —
  such pomp is valued there.

7 With joy approach, O Christian soul,
  do homage to your king;
  and highly praise his humble birth,
  and of his glory sing!

39/40 P Brooks
Tunes: Forest Green, Christmas Carol

1 O little town of Bethlehem,
  how still we see you lie!
  Above your deep and dreamless sleep
  the silent stars go by:
  yet in your dark streets shining
  is everlasting light;
  the hopes and fears of all the years
  are met in you tonight.

2 For Christ is born of Mary
  and, gathered all above
  while mortals sleep, the angels keep
  their watch of wondering love:
  O morning stars, together
  proclaim the holy birth,
  and praises sing to God the king,
  and peace to all the earth.

3 How silently, how silently
  the wondrous gift is given!
So God imparts to human hearts
  the blessings of his heaven:
no ear may hear his coming,
  but in this world of sin,
where meek souls will receive him —
  still the dear Christ enters in.

4 O holy child of Bethlehem,
  descend to us we pray;
cast out our sin and enter in,
  be born in us today!
We hear the Christmas angels
  the great glad tidings tell —
O come to us, abide with us,
  our Lord Emmanuel.

41 C F Alexander
Tune: Irby

1 Once in royal David's city
  stood a lowly cattle shed,
where a mother laid her baby
  in a manger for his bed:
Mary was that mother mild,
Jesus Christ, her little child.

2 He came down to earth from heaven
  who is God and Lord of all;
and his shelter was a stable
  and his cradle was a stall:
with the poor and meek and lowly
lived on earth our saviour holy.

3 And through all his wondrous childhood
  he would honour and obey,
love and watch the gentle mother
  in whose tender arms he lay:
Christian children all should be
kind, obedient, good as he.

4 For he is our childhood's pattern:
  day by day like us he grew;
he was little, weak and helpless —
  tears and smiles like us he knew:
and he feels for all our sadness,
and he shares in all our gladness.

5 And our eyes at last shall see him,
  through his own redeeming love;
for that child, so dear and gentle,
  is our Lord in heaven above:
and he leads his children on
to the place where he has gone.

6 Not in that poor lowly stable
  with the oxen standing by,
we shall see him, but in heaven,
  set at God's right hand on high:
there his children gather round
bright like stars, with glory crowned.

42 C G Rossetti
Tune: Cranham

1 In the bleak mid-winter
  frosty wind made moan,
earth stood hard as iron,
  water like a stone;
snow had fallen, snow on snow,
  snow on snow,
in the bleak mid-winter
  long ago.

2 Heaven cannot hold him,
  nor earth sustain;
heaven and earth shall flee away
  when he comes to reign:
in the bleak mid-winter
  a stable-place sufficed
God, the Lord almighty,
  Jesus Christ.

3 Enough for him whom cherubim
  worship night and day —
a breastful of milk,
  and a manger full of hay;
enough for him whom angels
  fall down before —
the wise men and the shepherds
  who adore!

4 What can I give him,
  poor as I am?
If I were a shepherd
  I would give a lamb,
if I were a wise man
  I would do my part;
yet what I can I give him —
  give my heart.

43 From the French, © Michael Perry †
Tune: Il est né

  Child of heaven born on earth —
  let the music sound his praises:
  Child of heaven born on earth —
  sing to greet the saviour's birth!

1 Christ, our hope, our joy, appears —
  for this time we have been waiting;
Christ our hope, our joy, appears —
  promise of a thousand years.
  Christ of heaven . . .

2 Cold within a lowly cave,
  tightly wrapped, in manger lying;
cold within a lowly cave
  is our God who stoops to save.
  Child of heaven . . .

3 Jesus, king and mighty one,
  gentle babe in Mary's keeping;
Jesus, king and mighty one,
  come to make our hearts your throne!
  Child of heaven . . .

44 © Timothy Dudley-Smith
Tune: Rhuddlan

1 Not in lordly state and splendour,
lofty pomp and high renown;
infant-form his robe most royal,
lantern-light his only crown;
    see the new-born King of glory,
    Lord of all to earth come down!

2 His no rich and storied mansion,
kingly rule and sceptred sway;
from his seat in highest heaven
throned among the beasts he lay:
    see the new-born King of glory
    cradled in his couch of hay!

3 Yet the eye of faith beholds him,
King above all earthly kings;
Lord of uncreated ages,
he whose praise eternal rings —
    see the new-born King of glory
    panoplied by angels' wings!

4 Not in lordly state and splendour,
lofty pomp and high renown;
infant-form his robe most royal,
lantern-light his only crown;
    Christ the new-born King of glory,
    Llord of all to earth come down!

45 After M MacDonald, L Macbean
Tune: Bunessan

1 Child in the manger, infant of Mary,
outcast and stranger, Lord of all!
child who inherits all our transgressions,
all our demerits on him fall.

2 Once the most holy child of salvation
gentle and lowly lived below:
now as our glorious mighty redeemer,
see him victorious over each foe.

3 Prophets foretold him, infant of wonder;
angels behold him on his throne:
worthy our saviour of all their praises;
happy for ever are his own.

46/47 © Timothy Dudley-Smith
Tunes: Morwenstow, Secret Birth

1 Child of the stable's secret birth,
the Lord by right of the lords of earth,
let angels sing of a king new-born,
the world is weaving a crown of thorn:
    a crown of thorn for that infant head
    cradled soft in the manger bed.

2 Eyes that shine in the lantern's ray;
a face so small in its nest of hay,
face of a child, who is born to scan
the world he made
        through the eyes of man:
    and from that face in the final day
    earth and heaven shall flee away.

3 Voice that rang through the courts on high
contracted now to a wordless cry,
a voice to master the wind and wave,
the human heart and the hungry grave:
    the voice of God through the cedar trees
    rolling forth as the sound of seas.

4 Infant hands in a mother's hand,
for none but Mary may understand
whose are the hands and the fingers curled
but his who fashioned
        and made our world:
    and through these hands
        in the hour of death
    nails shall strike to the wood beneath.

5 Child of the stable's secret birth,
the Father's gift to a wayward earth,
to drain the cup in a few short years
of all our sorrows, our sins and tears —
    ours the prize for the road he trod:
    risen with Christ; at peace with God.

48 West Indian Carol
Tune: Mary had a baby — sweet lamb

Mary had a baby —
    sweet lamb.
Where was he born?
Born in a manger —
    sweet lamb.
What did they call him?
Call him King Jesus,
    everlasting Father,
    mighty Prince of peace.
Mary had a baby —
    sweet lamb.

49 West Indian Carol
© in this version Word & Music †
Tune: Mary had a baby

1 Mary had a baby, yes Lord;
Mary had a baby, yes my Lord;
Mary had a baby, yes Lord!
    The people keep a-coming
for to see her child!
    (OR: but the train has gone!)

2 QUESTION:
What did she name him?
    yes, Lord . . .

3 ANSWER:
Mary named him Jesus!
    yes, Lord . . .

4 QUESTION:
Where was he born?
    yes, Lord . . .

5 ANSWER:
Born in a stable!
    yes, Lord . . .

6 QUESTION:
Where did she lay him?
yes, Lord . . .

7 ANSWER:
Laid him in a manger!
yes, Lord . . .

50/51 From the French, © Paul Wigmore †
Tune: Entre le boeuf et l'âne gris

1 Donkey and ox around his bed,
sleeps, sleeps, sleeps the little Boy:
angel hosts rejoice,
thousands with one voice
singing praise above
to this God of love.

2 Mary's the arms around him held,
sleeps, sleeps, sleeps the little Boy:
angel hosts rejoice . . .

3 Lily and rose around him spread,
sleeps, sleeps, sleeps the little Boy:
angel hosts rejoice . . .

4 There, on this glad and holy day,
sleeps, sleeps, sleeps the little Boy:
angel hosts rejoice . . .

52 J M Neale, © in this version Word & Music †
Tune: Resonet in laudibus

1 Christ is born for us today —
rough the manger, soft the hay;
all who will confess him may
receive the Son, the holy One of Mary.

2 Child of grace at Mary's knee,
he is born to set us free;
he is born our hope to be,
our God, our Lord, by all adored for ever.

3 Christians all, rejoice and sing
with the coming of our King;
let the bells of heaven ring
to tell the earth of Jesus's birth to Mary!

53 From the German, J Troutbeck
Tune: Vom Himmel hoch

Within this humble manger lies
the Lord who reigns above the skies;
within the stall where beasts have fed,
the virgin-born lays down his head.

54 © Christopher Porteous †
Tune: I see your crib

1 I see your crib —
a cradle where the cattle cry,
and in the stall you lie,
sweet Mary's holy boy.

The promise, and the love, God gives —
yet in the world around
no place for him is found.
'No room!' they cried —
our Lord was left outside.

2 I see your face,
so full of love in sleep —
and shepherds leave their sheep
to come and worship here.
Good news, which choirs of angels tell:
God's only, wondrous Son
to us on earth has come.
See where he lies in straw;
gaze, worship, and adore!

3 I see your star —
a guide, the way for men and kings,
the gift of God who brings
salvation from our sins,
to grow in grace with God and man.
He had no home, no bed:
'Come, follow me!' he said —
Lord, let me hear your call,
and bring my life, my all!

55/56 © Timothy Dudley-Smith
Tunes: Ruxley, Holy Child

1 Holy child, how still you lie!
safe the manger, soft the hay;
faint upon the eastern sky
breaks the dawn of Christmas Day.

2 Holy child, whose birthday brings
shepherds from their field and fold,
angel choirs and eastern kings,
myrrh and frankincense and gold:

3 Holy child, what gift of grace
from the Father freely willed!
In your infant form we trace
all God's promises fulfilled.

4 Holy child, whose human years
span like ours delight and pain;
one in human joys and tears,
one in all but sin and stain:

5 Holy child, so far from home,
all the lost to seek and save,
to what dreadful death you come,
to what dark and silent grave!

6 Holy child, before whose name
powers of darkness faint and fall;
conquered, death and sin and shame —
Jesus Christ is Lord of all!

7 Holy child, how still you lie!
safe the manger, soft the hay;
clear upon the eastern sky
breaks the dawn of Christmas Day.

57 Verses 1 and 2 unknown, verse 3 J T McFarland
Tune: Cradle Song

1 Away in a manger,
   no crib for a bed,
   the little Lord Jesus
   laid down his sweet head;
   the stars in the bright sky
   looked down where he lay;
   the little Lord Jesus
   asleep on the hay.

2 The cattle are lowing,
   the baby awakes,
   but little Lord Jesus
   no crying he makes:
   I love you, Lord Jesus —
   look down from on high
   and stay by my side
   until morning is nigh.

3 Be near me, Lord Jesus;
   I ask you to stay
   close by me for ever
   and love me, I pray;
   bless all the dear children
   in your tender care,
   and fit us for heaven
   to live with you there.

58 S Baring-Gould
Tune: The infant King

1 Sing lullaby!
   lullaby baby, now reclining:
      sing lullaby!
   Hush, do not wake the infant king;
   angels are watching, stars are shining
   over the place where he is lying:
      sing lullaby.

2 Sing lullaby!
   lullaby baby, sweetly sleeping:
      sing lullaby!
   Hush, do not wake the infant king;
   soon will come sorrow with the morning,
   soon will come bitter grief and weeping:
      sing lullaby!

3 Sing lullaby!
   lullaby baby, gently dozing:
      sing lullaby!
   Hush, do not wake the infant king;
   soon comes the cross, the nails,
      the piercing,
   then in the grave at last reposing:
      sing lullaby!

4 Sing lullaby!
   lullaby! Is the baby waking?
      sing lullaby!
   Hush, do not stir the infant king,
   dreaming of Easter, joyful morning,
   conquering death, its bondage breaking:
      sing lullaby!

59 From the German, J Davies
© in this version Word & Music †
Tune: Schlaf wohl

1 O slumber, heaven-born treasure, now
   sleep softly holy child,
   as shepherds poor before you bow,
   on whom the angel smiled:
   with tender love they join to sing
   a lullaby to heaven's king.
      Lullaby, lullaby,
      sleep, sleep softly, lullaby.

2 For Mary, with her loving hands
   has laid you down to sleep,
   while Joseph by your cradle stands
   his faithful watch to keep;
   there on the straw the oxen mild
   are lying still — sleep holy child!
      Lullaby . . .

3 When you are grown you shall be great —
   but then comes Calvary,
   where men shall seize you in their hate
   and nail you to a tree!
   but sweetest dreams be yours tonight —
   sleep holy child till morning light!
      Lullaby . . .

60 Based on the Latin, © Michael Perry †
Tune: Dormi Jesu

1 Sleep, Lord Jesus! Mary smiling
   on her infant so beguiling
      sings a joyful lullaby.

2 Sleep, Lord Jesus! Mary grieving
   at the fate our sin is weaving
      sings a solemn lullaby.

3 Sleep, Lord Jesus! Mary dreaming
   of this fallen world's redeeming
      sings a holy lullaby.

   Sleep, Lord Jesus, Lullaby!

61 © Paul Wigmore †
Tune: O Waly Waly

1 I saw my love by lantern light,
   my newborn child so frail and fair,
   and through the toils of that long night,
   I saw my love all lonely there.

2 I saw my love by morning light,
   this holy boy, so sweet and fair,
   and in his eyes I saw the sight
   of all the earth in anguish there.

3 I saw my love by noonday light,
   the King of love, so strong and fair,
   and in his hands I saw the might
   of all the powers of heaven there.

4 I saw my love by evening light,
   the sinner's friend, so young and fair,
   and in his death I saw no fright
   but life eternal springing there.

5 I saw my love by lantern light,
   my newborn child so frail and fair,
   and through the toils of that long night
   I saw my love all loving there.

62/63
© Paul Wigmore †
Tune: Es wird scho glei dumpa

1 The daylight is fading,
      the evening is near:
   O Child in the manger,
      there's nothing to fear;
   I'll stand by your cradle
      this holy night long,
   I'll sing to you softly —
      so sleep to my song,
      little Child, little Child,
      so sleep to my song!

2 The starlight is coming —
      the dawning of pain,
   the anguish, the sorrow
      for souls to regain:
   but angels bring joy
      to your Bethlehem night —
   no palace was lit
      by such heavenly light,
      little Child, little Child,
      so sleep to my song!

64
© Michael Perry †
Tune: Rocking

1 Jesus, saviour, holy child,
      sleep tonight,
   slumber deep till morning light.
      Lullaby, our joy, our treasure,
      all our hope and all our pleasure:
   at the cradle where you lie
   we will worship — Lullaby!

2 From your Father's home you come
      to this earth,
   by your lowly manger birth!
      Child of God, our nature sharing;
      Son of Man, our sorrows bearing;
   rich, yet here among the poor:
   Christ the Lord, whom we adore!

3 Now to heaven's glory song
      we reply
   with a Christmas lullaby.
      Hush, the eternal Lord is sleeping
      close in Mary's tender keeping:
   babe on whom the angels smiled —
   Jesus, saviour, holy child.

65
After S Scheidt, © Michael Perry †
Tune: O Jesulein süss

1 O Jesus my Lord, how sweetly you lie
   so far from home in heaven on high:
   you come to do the Father's will,
   to feel our pain, to cure our ill,
   to live and serve, to love and die!

2 O Jesus my Lord, how sweetly you lie —
   a helpless babe in poverty:
   you deign to share our earthly fate,
   and by your grace illuminate
   the valley of our misery!

3 O Jesus my Lord, how sweetly you lie —
   the Son revealed to human eye:
   so light in us your flame of love
   that we may lift our hearts above
   to him whom angels glorify!

4 O Jesus my Lord, how sweetly you lie
   and show us God's humility:
   accept the offering at our hands
   of faithfulness to your commands,
   and praise throughout eternity!

66
G R Woodward, © in this version Word & Music †
Tune: Susanni

1 Descend from heaven, you angels bright —
      Alleluia;
      Lullaby, lullaby, lullaby!
   to greet with song this holy night —
      Alleluia, alleluia!
   and tell of Jesus, Mary's Son.

2 Come, greet our world
      with tuneful voice —
      Alleluia;
      Lullaby, lullaby, lullaby!
   with high celestial praise rejoice —
      Alleluia, alleluia!
   and tell of Jesus, Mary's Son.

3 So let your cheerful music sound —
      Alleluia;
      Lullaby, lullaby, lullaby!
   until the very skies resound —
      Alleluia, alleluia!
   in praise of Jesus, Mary's Son.

4 Sing, 'Peace, good-will
      from shore to shore —
      Alleluia;
      Lullaby, lullaby, lullaby!
   on high sing glory evermore' —
      Alleluia, alleluia!
   in praise of Jesus, Mary's Son.

67 Fifteenth century carol
© in this version Word & Music †
Tune: Old Basque Noël

1 I heard a mother tenderly sing —
   she cradled her child with gentle rocking:
   Lullay, lullay, my dear son,
      my sweet one;
   lullay, lullay, my dear son,
      my own dear darling!

2 This is the Lord who made all things,
   and he is our God — the King of all kings.
   Lullay, lullay . . .

3 There was sweet music at Jesus' birth
   from angels
      who sang to greet the whole earth.
   Lullay, lullay . . .

4 Come, let us sing and come, let us pray
   that peace may be ours upon this glad day.
   Lullay, lullay . . .

68 © Michael Perry †
Tune: Deus tuorum militum

1 Glad music fills the Christmas sky —
   a hymn of praise, a song of love;
   the angels worship high above
   and Mary sings her lullaby.

2 Of tender love for God she sings,
   the chosen mother of the Son;
   she knows that wonders have begun,
   and trusts for all the future brings.

3 The angel chorus of the skies
   who come to tell us of God's grace
   have yet to know his human face,
   to watch him die, to see him rise.

4 Let praise be true and love sincere,
   rejoice to greet the saviour's birth;
   let peace and honour fill the earth
   and mercy reign — for God is here!

5 Then lift your hearts and voices high,
   sing once again the Christmas song:
   for love and praise to Christ belong —
   in shorts of joy, and lullaby.

69 © Paul Wigmore †
Tune: Geborn ist uns ein Kindelein

1 Travellers all to Bethlehem,
   they sing for me and I for them;
   the song they sing is all forlorn,
   and mine is of a baby born.
      O hear the song I sing today —
      that Christ is with us on our way.

2 Beautiful child upon my breast,
   of all my songs I'll sing the best:
   my lullaby this holy morn
   is for a holy saviour born.
      O hear the song . . .

3 Shepherd boy, with your eyes so bright
   to see a king by lantern light,
   let your sweet voice with mine adorn
   this wondrous day when Christ is born.
      O hear the song . . .

4 Travellers from the East come down
   to find this king without a crown!
   The crown he'll wear no king has worn,
   to wear this crown the Christ is born.
      O hear the song . . .

70 From the Latin, J M Neale
Tune: In dulci jubilo

1 Good Christians all, rejoice
   with heart and soul and voice!
   listen now to what we say,
   Jesus Christ is born today;
   ox and ass before him bow
   and he is in the manger now:
      Christ is born today;
      Christ is born today!

2 Good Christians all, rejoice
   with heart and soul and voice!
   hear the news of endless bliss,
   Jesus Christ was born for this:
   he has opened heaven's door
   and we are blessed for evermore:
      Christ was born for this;
      Christ was born for this!

3 Good Christians all, rejoice
   with heart and soul and voice!
   now you need not fear the grave;
   Jesus Christ was born to save:
   come at his most gracious call
   to find salvation, one and all:
      Christ was born to save;
      Christ was born to save!

71 A Gregory Murray
© 1956 J Curwen and Sons Limited
Sole selling agents William Elkin Music Services
Tune: Pieds en l'air

1 Come to Bethlehem
      and see the new-born king,
   come and lay your heart before him
      while you sing:
   he, the God of earth and heaven,
      Lord of all,
   lies within the manger of an ox's stall;
   born of God the Father in the bliss above,
   born a baby in a stable for our love.

2 He, the Lord of all before our race began,
   loves to be and call himself the Son of Man;
   holy Mary, virgin mother, gave him birth —
   see her meekly kneel before him
      on the earth.
   Let us kneel with her and lovingly adore
   Christ her son,
      our God and king for evermore!

72 From the Latin, © Michael Perry †
Tune: Gaudete

Rejoice with heart and voice!
now is our Saviour
of the virgin Mary born —
so rejoice!

1 At this time our God fulfils
all our expectation:
let us offer hearts and wills
in rededication.
Rejoice . . .

2 God of God when time began,
Lord of all creation:
we revere the Son of Man
at his incarnation.
Rejoice . . .

3 Alleluia! Let us sing
hymns of adoration,
blessing Christ our worthy king
in this celebration!
Rejoice . . .

73 C Wordsworth, © in this version Word & Music †
Tune: England's Lane

1 Sing, oh sing, this happy morn,
for to us a child is born,
and to us a Son is given;
God comes down to earth from heaven:
Sing, oh sing, this happy morn,
Jesus Christ today is born!

2 God of God, and Light of light,
comes with mercies infinite
joining — in a wondrous plan —
heaven to earth, and God to man:
Sing, oh sing

3 God with us, Emmanuel,
deigns for ever now to dwell —
now on Adam's fallen race
sends the fulness of his grace:
Sing, oh sing

4 Go comes down that we may rise,
lifted up into the skies;
Christ is Son of Man, that we
children of our God may be:
Sing, oh sing

5 Come, renew us Lord, we pray,
with your Spirit day by day;
that we ever may be one
with the Father and the Son.
Sing, oh sing

74 From the Latin, © Michael Perry †
Tune: Resonet in laudibus (i)

1 Christians, make a joyful sound,
sing to all the world around:
he is in a manger found,
the holy One, the infant son of Mary.

Let the people join to say
that Christ the Lord is born today,
till the very earth shall raise
the song of praise:
'Nowell, nowell —
Christ is born, the infant son of Mary!'

2 Mighty God, Emmanuel —
prince of whom the prophets tell,
child announced by Gabriel,
the holy One, the infant son of Mary.
Let the people . . .

3 Come, you choirs, with gladness sing,
instruments of music bring —
eager to proclaim the king,
the holy One, the infant son of Mary.
Let the people . . .

4 Love is here to seek and save —
heaven's master as a slave:
God so loved the world he gave
the holy One, the infant son of Mary.
Let the people . . .

75 After Prudentius; J M Neale and H W Baker
© in this version Jubilate Hymns †
Tune: Corde natus

1 God of God, the uncreated,
love before the world began;
Christ the source and Christ the ending,
Son of God and Son of Man,
Lord of all the things that have been,
master of the eternal plan,
evermore and evermore.

2 He is here, whom generations
sought throughout the ages long;
promised by the ancient prophets,
justice for a world of wrong,
God's salvation for the faithful:
him we praise in endless song . . .

3 Happy is that day for ever
when, by God the Spirit's grace,
lowly Mary, virgin mother,
bore the saviour of our race.
Man and child, the world's redeemer
now displays his sacred face . . .

4 Praise him, heaven of the heavens,
praise him, angels in the height;
priests and prophets, bow before him,
saints who longed to see this sight.
Let no human voice be silent,
in his glory hearts unite . . .

5 Christ be praised with God the Father,
and the Holy Spirit, praised!
hymns of worship, high thanksgiving
echo through a world amazed:
Honour, majesty, dominion!
songs of victory be raised . . .

76
From *Piae Cantiones*, G R Woodward
© in this version Word & Music †
Tune: Ding-dong ding

Ding-dong, ding,
ding-a-dong-a-ding;
ding-dong, ding-dong,
ding-a-dong-ding.

1 Wake then, Christian, come and listen
how the merry church bells ring
and from steeple call the people
to adore the new-born king:

2 Tell the story how from glory
God came down at Christmastide,
bringing gladness, chasing sadness,
showering blessings far and wide.

3 Child of mother, like no other —
of the virgin Mary born,
to a stable — this no fable —
God came down on Christmas morn.

(Ding-dong . . .)

77
N Tate
Tune: Winchester Old

1 While shepherds watched their flocks
by night,
all seated on the ground,
the angel of the Lord came down
and glory shone around.

2 'Fear not,' said he — for mighty dread
had seized their troubled mind —
'Glad tidings of great joy I bring
to you and all mankind:

3 'To you in David's town this day
is born of David's line
a saviour, who is Christ the Lord.
And this shall be the sign:

4 'The heavenly babe you there shall find
to human view displayed,
all tightly wrapped in swathing bands
and in a manger laid.'

5 Thus spoke the seraph, and forthwith
appeared a shining throng
of angels praising God, who thus
addressed their joyful song:

6 'All glory be to God on high,
and to the earth be peace;
goodwill henceforth from highest heaven
begin and never cease!'

78
Traditional
Tune: Go, tell it on the mountain

Go, tell it on the mountain,
over the hills and everywhere;
go, tell it on the mountain
that Jesus Christ is born!

1 While shepherds sat a-watching
their silent flocks by night,
there shone throughout the heavens
a great and glorious light.
Go, tell . . .

2 The shepherds feared and trembled
when, high above the earth,
rang out the angel chorus
that hailed our Saviour's birth.
Go, tell . . .

79
After M Luther, © Michael Perry †
Tune: Echo Carol

1 From highest heaven where praises ring
(from highest heaven where praises ring)
good news I bring (good news I bring),
songs to sing (songs to sing):
'Jesus is born to be your king!'
('Jesus is born to be your king!')

2 He who in majesty arrayed
(he who in majesty arrayed),
without our aid (without our aid),
all has made (all has made):
see him in humble manger laid,
(see him in humble manger laid).

3 Let human power and pomp and pride
(let human power and pomp and pride),
both far and wide (both far and wide),
be denied (be denied):
God is come down at Christmastide
(God is come down at Christmastide)!

4 To God the Father, Spirit, Son
(to God the Father, Spirit, Son),
the Three-in-One (the Three-in-One),
praise be done (praise be done)
for grace and hope this day begun
(for grace and hope this day begun)!

80
After J Möhr, J F Young
Tune: Stille nacht

1 Silent night! holy night!
all is calm, all is bright
round the virgin and her child:
holy infant, so gentle and mild,
sleep in heavenly peace;
sleep in heavenly peace!

2 Silent night! holy night!
shepherds quail at the sight,
glory streams from heaven afar:
heavenly hosts sing, 'Alleluia,
Christ the saviour is born,
Christ the saviour is born.'

3 Silent night! holy night!
Son of God, love's pure light:
radiant beams your holy face
with the dawn of saving grace,
Jesus, Lord, at your birth,
Jesus, Lord, at your birth.

81/82
J Anstice
© in this version Word & Music †
Tunes: Bellman's Carol, St Stephen

1 When came in flesh the incarnate Word,
the heedless world slept on,
and only watching shepherds heard
the news of God's own Son.

2 When comes the Saviour at the last,
from east to west shall shine
his awesome light; the earth aghast
shall tremble at the sign.

3 Then shall the pure in heart be blessed —
in peace he'll come to them
as once he lay at Mary's breast
in distant Bethlehem:

4 In peace, to humble love and faith,
and yet more strong to save;
more strong by having bowed to death,
by having burst the grave.

5 Lord, who could dare see you descend
in state, unless he knew
you are the sorrowing sinner's friend,
the gracious and the true?

6 Dwell in our hearts, O Saviour blessed:
so shall your advent's dawn
become the knowing of love's guest,
the veil of night withdrawn!

83
From the Polish, E M G Reed
Tune: Infant holy

1 Infant holy, infant lowly,
for his bed a cattle stall;
oxen lowing, little knowing
Christ the babe is Lord of all.
Swift are winging angels singing,
nowells ringing, tidings bringing:
Christ the babe is Lord of all;
Christ the babe is Lord of all!

2 Flocks were sleeping, shepherds keeping
vigil till the morning new,
saw the glory, heard the story —
tidings of a gospel true.
Thus rejoicing, free from sorrow,
praises voicing greet tomorrow:
Christ the babe was born for you;
Christ the babe was born for you!

84
C Wesley and others
Tune: Mendelssohn

1 Hark! the herald angels sing
glory to the new-born King;
peace on earth and mercy mild,
God and sinners reconciled!
Joyful all you nations rise,
join the triumph of the skies;
with the angelic host proclaim,

'Christ is born in Bethlehem':
Hark! the herald angels sing
glory to the new-born King.

2 Christ, by highest heaven adored,
Christ, the everlasting Lord:
late in time behold him come,
offspring of a virgin's womb;
veiled in flesh the Godhead see,
hail the incarnate Deity!
pleased as man with us to dwell,
Jesus our Emmanuel:
Hark! the herald . . .

3 Hail the heaven-born Prince of peace,
hail the Sun of righteousness;
light and life to all he brings,
risen with healing in his wings:
mild, he lays his glory by,
born that we no more may die;
born to raise us from the earth,
born to give us second birth:
Hark! the herald . . .

85
After the Jugoslavian Carol, © Michael Perry †
Tune: Rajske strune zadonite

1 Hear the skies around
fill with joyful sound,
and the praise of angels ring;
hear the skies . . .
  Singing 'Glory in the highest,'
  singing 'Glory to the King!'
Hear the skies . . .

2 'To the earth be peace,
fear and sorrow cease!'
is the birthday news they bring.
'To the earth . . .
  Singing 'Glory in the highest,'
  singing 'Glory to the King!'
'To the earth . . .

3 Banish all dismay,
for on Christmas day
there's a song of hope to sing;
banish all . . .
  Singing 'Glory in the highest,'
  singing 'Glory to the King!'
Banish all . . .

86
J Montgomery, © in this version Jubilate Hymns †
Tune: Iris

1 Angels from the realms of glory,
wing your flight through all the earth;
heralds of creation's story
now proclaim Messiah's birth!
  Come and worship
  Christ, the new-born king:
  come and worship,
  worship Christ the new-born king.

2 Shepherds in the fields abiding,
   watching by your flocks at night,
   God with us is now residing:
   see, there shines the infant light!
   Come and worship . . .

3 Wise men, leave your contemplations!
   brighter visions shine afar;
   seek in him the hope of nations,
   you have seen his natal star:
   Come and worship . . .

4 Though an infant now we view him,
   he will share his Father's throne,
   gather all the nations to him;
   every knee shall then bow down:
   Come and worship . . .

87/88
© Paul Wigmore †
Tune: The Angels and the Shepherds

1 BOY SOLO
   Softly, a shepherd is singing his song
   over the Bethlehem hills all night long:
      ALL
      Night-time is passing —
      wait for the dawning!
      Praise him who brings us
      joy in the morning:
      Alleluia!

2 ALL
   Heralding angels are singing their song,
   wonderful words that to heaven belong:
   Night-time is passing . . .

3 SOPRANO
   Lovingly, Mary is singing her song,
   bearing the child
      who will bear all our wrong:
      ALL Night-time is passing . . .

4 ALL
   Worshipping Jesus, we sing a new song —
   Bethlehem's baby, our saviour so strong:
   Night-time is passing . . .

89/90
After P Gerhardt, C Winkworth
© in this version Word & Music †
Tunes: Bonn, All my heart

1 All my heart this night rejoices,
   as I hear, far and near,
   sweetest angel voices.
   'Christ is born!' their choirs are singing,
   till the air everywhere
   now with joy is ringing.

2 Listen! from a humble manger
   comes the call, 'One and all,
   run from sin and danger!
   Christians come, let nothing grieve you:
   you are freed! All you need
   I will surely give you.'

3 Gather, then, from every nation;
   here let all, great and small,
   kneel in adoration;
   love him who with love is yearning:
   Hail the star that from far
   bright with hope is burning!

4 You, my Lord, with love I'll cherish,
   live to you, and with you
   dying, shall not perish,
   but shall dwell with you for ever
   far on high, in the joy
   that can alter never.

91
After Sedulius and J Ellerton;
© in this version Word & Music †
Tune: This endris nyght

1 From east to west, from shore to shore,
   let earth awake and sing:
   the holy child that Mary bore
   is Christ, the Lord and King!

2 He did not spurn the ox's stall,
   nor scorn the manger bed;
   there God whose mercy feeds us all,
   at Mary's breast was fed.

3 For us the world's Creator wears
   the fashion of a slave;
   our human flesh the Maker shares,
   his creature, comes to save.

4 To shepherds poor, their Lord most high —
   their Shepherd — was revealed,
   while angel choirs sang in the sky
   across the silent field:

5 All glory be to God above,
   and on the earth be peace
   to all who long to taste his love,
   till time itself shall cease!

92
E H Sears, © in this version Jubilate Hymns †
Tune: Noel

1 It came upon the midnight clear,
   that glorious song of old,
   from angels bending near the earth
   to touch their harps of gold:
   'Peace on the earth, goodwill to men
   from heaven's all-gracious king!'
   The world in solemn stillness lay
   to hear the angels sing.

2 With sorrow brought by sin and strife
   the world has suffered long
   and, since the angels sang, have passed
   two thousand years of wrong;
   for man at war with man hears not
   the love-song which they bring:
   O hush the noise, you men of strife,
   and hear the angels sing!

3 And those whose journey now is hard,
whose hope is burning low,
who tread the rocky path of life
with painful steps and slow:
O listen to the news of love
which makes the heavens ring!
O rest beside the weary road
and hear the angels sing!

4 And still the days are hastening on —
by prophets seen of old —
towards the fulness of the time
when comes the age foretold:
then earth and heaven renewed shall see
the prince of peace, their king;
and all the world repeat the song
which now the angels sing.

93
© Timothy Dudley-Smith
Tune: Rectory Meadow

1 O Prince of peace whose promised birth
the angels sang with 'Peace on earth,'
peace be to us and all beside,
    peace to us all —
peace to the world this Christmastide.

2 O Child who found to lay your head
no place but in a manger bed,
come where our doors stand open wide,
    peace to us all —
    peace to the world —
peace in our homes this Christmastide.

3 O Christ whom shepherds came to find,
their joy be ours in heart and mind;
let grief and care be laid aside,
    peace to us all —
    peace to the world —
    peace in our homes —
peace in our hearts this Christmastide.

4 O Saviour Christ, ascended Lord,
our risen Prince of life restored,
our Love who once for sinners died,
    peace to us all —
    peace to the world —
    peace in our homes —
    peace in our hearts —
peace with our God this Christmastide!

94
From the German, © Paul Wigmore †
Tune: O du fröhliche

1 Holy, joyful dawn of Christmas,
love to each unworthy heart,
    Jesus bringing
    new beginning,
love to earth in every part.

2 Holy, joyful dawn of Christmas,
joy to each unworthy heart,
    Christ abiding,
    sinners guiding,
joy to earth in every part.

3 Holy, joyful dawn of Christmas,
peace to each unworthy heart,
    angels raising,
    heaven's praising,
peace to earth in every part.

95
After Germanus, J M Neale;
© in this version Word & Music †
Tune: Est ist ein' ros'

1 A great and mighty wonder:
redemption drawing near!
the virgin bears the infant,
the prince of peace is here!
Repeat the hymn again:
    'To God on high . . .

2 The Word becomes incarnate
and yet remains on high;
the shepherds hear the anthem
as glory fills the sky —
repeat the hymn again:
    'To God on high . . .

3 The angels sing the story:
awake, O distant lands!
Rejoice, you hills and valleys,
you oceans, clap your hands!
Repeat the hymn again:
    'To God on high . . .

4 He comes to save all nations:
let all now hear his word!
approach and bring him worship,
the saviour and the Lord!
Repeat the hymn again:
    'To God on high . . .

96
From the German, © Paul Wigmore †
Tune: Still, still, still

1 Still, still, still,
the baby lies asleep:
yet far away are herald voices —
heaven sings and earth rejoices!
Still, still, still,
the baby lies asleep.

2 Love, love, love,
no greater love than his;
while 'Christ the Lord'
    the angels name him,
we with fervent hearts acclaim him.
Love, love, love,
no greater love than his!

97 © Paul Wigmore †
Tune: God is in Bethlehem

1 God to Adam came in Eden,
heaven flowered at his feet;
all creation sang together,
new-born man on earth to greet.
Stars beaming bright, still of the night,
cry of an angel, splendour of light
shining on Bethlehem:
God is in Bethlehem!

2 Eve to Adam came in Eden,
nature blossomed at their side;
bound in love and blessed in union,
perfect man and purest bride.
Stars beaming bright . . .

3 Sin to Adam came in Eden,
heaven sorrowed in its heart;
tears of grief its garden drowning,
thorns of death in every part.
Stars beaming bright . . .

4 God to us has come a saviour,
grace to sinners on the earth;
shepherds greet the infant Jesus,
God and man in virgin birth.
Stars beaming bright . . .

98 Traditional, © in this version, Word & Music †
Tune: Sussex Carol

1 Good Christian people, rise and sing
to greet the news the angels bring;
good Christian people, rise and sing
to greet the news the angels bring:
news of great joy for all the earth,
news of our holy saviour's birth!

2 Rejoice and be no longer sad,
for Christ is born to make us glad;
rejoice and be no longer sad,
for Christ is born to make us glad:
his power will drive away our sin,
his lowly birth our love shall win.

3 Now in our darkness shines the light
which made the angels sing that night;
now in our darkness shines the light
which made the angels sing that night.
Glory to God! goodwill and peace
be to us all, and never cease!

99 G R Woodward
Tune: Branle de l'Official

1 Ding dong! Merrily on high
in heaven the bells are ringing.
Ding dong! Verily the sky
is riven with angels singing:
Gloria, hosanna in excelsis;
gloria, hosanna in excelsis!

2 E'en so here below, below,
let steeple bells be swungen;
and i-o, i-o, i-o,
by priest and people sungen!
Gloria . . .

3 Pray you, dutifully prime
your matin chime, you ringers;
may you beautifully rhyme
your evetime song, you singers:
Gloria . . .

100 © Michael Perry †
Tune: I saw three ships

1 ALL
When God from heaven
to earth came down
on Christmas Day, on Christmas Day,
the songs rang out in Bethlehem town
on Christmas Day in the morning.

2 WOMEN AND GIRLS
For Christ was born to save us all,
on Christmas Day, on Christmas Day,
and laid within a manger stall
on Christmas Day in the morning.

3 MEN AND BOYS
The shepherds heard the angels sing
on Christmas Day, on Christmas Day,
to tell them of the saviour-king
on Christmas Day in the morning.

4 ALL
Now joy is ours and all is well,
on Christmas Day, on Christmas Day,
so sound the organ, chime the bell
on Christmas Day in the morning!

101 © Michael Perry †
Tune: All through the night

1 Come and sing the Christmas story
this holy night!
Christ is born: the hope of glory
dawns on our sight.
Alleluia! earth is ringing
with a thousand angels singing —
hear the message they are bringing
this holy night.

2 Jesus, Saviour, child of Mary
this holy night,
in a world confused and weary
you are our light.
God is in a manger lying,
manhood taking, self denying,
life embracing, death defying
this holy night.

3 Lord of all! Let us acclaim him
    this holy night;
  king of our salvation name him,
    throned in the height.
  Son of Man — let us adore him,
  all the earth is waiting for him;
  Son of God — we bow before him
    this holy night.

102/103 After J F Wade;
F Oakeley and others

Tune: Adeste fideles
*Verses 3 and 4 are frequently omitted

1 O come, all ye faithful,
  joyful and triumphant;
  O come ye, O come ye to Bethlehem;
  come and behold him,
      born the king of angels!
  O come, let us adore him,
  O come, let us adore him,
  O come, let us adore him,
  Christ the Lord!

2 God from God,
  Light from light —
  lo, he abhors not the virgin's womb!
  Very God, begotten, not created.
  O come . . .

3 See how the shepherds
  summoned to his cradle,
  leaving their flocks,
      draw nigh with lowly fear:
  we too will thither
      bend our joyful footsteps.
  O come . . .

4 Led by the starlight,
  Magi, Christ adoring,
  offer him incense, gold, and myrrh;
  we to the Christ-child
      bring our hearts' oblations.
  O come . . .

5 Child, for us sinners,
  poor and in the manger,
  we would embrace thee
      with love and awe:
  who could not love thee,
      loving us so dearly?
  O come . . .

6 Sing, choirs of angels,
  sing in exultation!
  Sing, all ye citizens of heaven above,
  'Glory to God in the highest!'
  O come . . .

7 Yea, Lord, we greet thee,
  born for our salvation;
  Jesus, to thee be glory given!
  Word of the Father
      now in flesh appearing.
  O come . . .

OR, ON CHRISTMAS DAY:

7 Yea, Lord, we greet thee,
  born this happy morning;
  Jesus, to thee be glory given!
  Word of the Father
      now in flesh appearing.
  O come . . .

104/105 From the German
© Paul Wigmore †

Tune: Ihr Kinderlein kommet

1 O come all you children
      to Bethlehem town,
  and see here a baby
      from heaven come down;
  tread softly and enter on this sacred night
  a stable with heavenly glory alight.

2 O come all you children,
      come here to the stall
  and see here a child
      who is born Lord of all;
  more fair than the angels in glory is he,
  more lovely than cherubim ever could be.

3 O come all you children,
      and stand by his bed,
  and see gentle Mary bend low at his head;
  see Joseph, so humble in wondering joy,
  kneel down
      at the feet of this most holy boy.

4 O come then, you children,
      and hark at the throng
  of angels, all crowding the sky
      with their song;
  join in with their praises and joyfully sing
  your loudest thanksgiving —
      for Jesus the king!

106 © Michael Perry †
Tune: Nos Galan

1 Come and hear the joyful singing,
      Alleluia, gloria,
  set the bells of heaven ringing:
      alleluia, gloria,
  God the Lord has shown us favour —
      alleluia, gloria,
  Christ is born to be our saviour.
      Alleluia, gloria!

2 Angels of his birth are telling,
      Alleluia, gloria,
  prince of peace all powers excelling;
      alleluia, gloria,
  death and hell can not defeat him:
      alleluia, gloria,
  go to Bethlehem and greet him.
      Alleluia, gloria!

3 Choir and people, shout in wonder,
   Alleluia, gloria,
   let the merry organ thunder;
   alleluia, gloria,
   thank our God for love amazing,
   alleluia, gloria,
   Father, Son and Spirit praising.
   Alleluia, gloria!

107 © Michael Perry †
Tune: Marston St Lawrence

1 Lift your heart and raise your voice;
   faithful people, come, rejoice:
   grace and power are shown on earth
   in the saviour's holy birth.
   Gloria!

2 Mortals, hear what angels say;
   shepherds, quickly make your way,
   finding truth in lowly guise,
   wisdom to confound the wise.
   Gloria!

3 Here he lies, the Lord of all;
   nature's king in cattle-stall,
   God of heaven to earth come down —
   cross for throne and thorn for crown.
   Gloria!

4 Lift your hearts and voices high;
   then shall glory fill the sky,
   Christ shall come and not be long,
   earth shall sing the angels' song:
   'Gloria!'

108 Traditional, © in this version Word & Music †
Tune: Rise up shepherd and follow

1 There's a Saviour to see
      on Christmas morn —
   rise up, shepherd, and follow;
   we will show you the place
      where the Child is born —
   rise up, shepherd, and follow!

   Leave your sheep
   and leave your lambs —
   rise up, shepherd, and follow:
   leave your sheep
   and leave your rams —
   rise up, shepherd, and follow!

   Follow, follow,
   rise up, shepherd, and follow;
   hark to the angels of Bethlehem —
   rise up, shepherd,
      and follow, follow, follow!

2 If you take good heed
      to the angel's words —
   rise up, shepherd, and follow;
   you'll forget your flocks,
      you'll forget your herds —
   rise up, shepherd, and follow!

Leave your sheep . . .

109 From the French, John Rutter
© Oxford University Press
and in this version Word & Music †
Tune: Quittez, pasteurs

1 O leave your sheep,
   where ewes with lambs are feeding;
   you shepherds, hear
   our message of good cheer.
   No longer weep;
   the angel tidings heeding,
   to Bethlehem haste away.
      Our Lord, our Lord,
      our Lord is born this happy day.
      Our Lord . . .

2 For Love lies there
   within a lowly manger —
   the infant poor
   whom angel hosts adore!
   Such perfect care
   has saved us all from danger
   and brought us to the fold.
      Now see, now see,
      God's faithful love revealed of old.
      Now see . . .

3 You wise men three,
   arrayed in royal splendour,
   true homage pay:
   your king is born today!
   The star you see
   its radiance must surrender
   before our Sun most bright,
      Your gifts, your gifts,
      your gifts are precious in his sight.
      Your gifts . . .

4 O Spirit blessed,
   the source of life eternal,
   our souls inspire
   with your celestial fire!
   We make our guest
   the Christ, the Lord supernal,
   and sing the peace on earth
      God gives, God gives,
      God gives us by this holy birth;
      God gives . . .

110/111 © Michael Perry †
Tune: Calypso Carol

1 See him lying on a bed of straw:
   a draughty stable with an open door;
   Mary cradling the babe she bore —
   the prince of glory is his name.
      O now carry me to Bethlehem
      to see the Lord appear to men —
      just as poor as was the stable then,
      the prince of glory when he came.

2 Star of silver, sweep across the skies,
   show where Jesus in the manger lies;
   shepherds, swiftly from your stupor rise
   to see the saviour of the world!
      O now carry me to Bethlehem
      to see the Lord appear to men —
      just as poor as was the stable then,
      the prince of glory when he came.

3 Angels, sing again the song you sang,
   bring God's glory to the heart of man;
   sing that Bethl'em's little baby can
   be salvation to the soul.
      O now carry . . .

4 Mine are riches, from your poverty,
   from your innocence, eternity;
   mine forgiveness by your death for me,
   child of sorrow for my joy.
      O now carry . . .

112 Verse 1 L H Ward, © 1952 Boston Music Co Inc, c/o Chappell Music/International Music Publications; verse 2 © Jubilee Hymns †
Tune: Saltash

1 Little children, wake and listen!
   songs are filling all the earth;
   while the stars in heaven glisten,
   hear the news of Jesus' birth.
   Long ago, to lonely meadows
   angels brought the message down;
   still each year through midnight shadows
   it is heard in every town.

2 Shepherds hurry to the stable
   by the inn at Bethlehem,
   run as fast as they are able
   to the baby born for them.
   People find the news amazing
   as on that first Christmas morn:
   let us join the shepherds praising
   God, for Christ the king is born!

113 After B de la Monnoye, © Paul Wigmore †
Tune: Patapan

1 Bethlehem, we come to bring
   merry dances for your king!
      Step by step and drum by drum,
      pat-a-pat-a-pan, pat-a-pat-a-pan;
      step by step and drum by drum
      stepping bravely, here we come!

2 Mary, may we come to sing
   merry songs to Christ our king?
      Step by step . . .
      stepping softly, here we come!

3 Christian people, now we say
   merry Christmas on this day!
      Step by step . . .
      stepping gladly, here we come!

114 © Michael Perry †
Tune: Russian Air

1 Christ is born within a stable:
      greet the day when heaven smiled!
   Shepherds, fast as they are able,
      run to see the holy Child.
      Alleluia, alleluia,
      alleluia! Amen.

2 Eastern skies are brightly shining,
      hope has come upon the earth;
   angel songs with ours combining
      tell the world of Jesus' birth.
      Alleluia, alleluia,
      alleluia! Amen.

3 Peal the bells and set them ringing,
      spread the joyful news abroad;
   come with faith and join our singing
      to acclaim the incarnate Lord!
      Alleluia, alleluia,
      alleluia! Amen.

115 M Sargent, © Oxford University Press and in this version Word & Music †
Tune: Zither Carol

1 Girls and boys, leave your toys,
      make no noise,
   kneel at his crib and worship him.
   For this shrine, Child divine, is the sign
   our Saviour's here.
      Alleluia, the church bells ring,
      'Alleluia!' the angels sing,
      alleluia from everything —
   all must draw near!

2 On that day, far away, Jesus lay —
   angels were watching round his head.
   Holy Child, mother mild, undefiled,
   we sing your praise.
      Alleluia . . .
   our hearts we raise.

3 Shepherds came at the fame of your name,
   angels their guide to Bethlehem;
   in that place
      saw your face filled with grace,
   stood at your door.
      Alleluia . . .
   love evermore.

116 From the French, © Paul Wigmore †
Tune: French carol melody

1 Shepherd-boy, tell me,
      why are you singing;
   shepherd-boy, tell me, what is your song?
   Glory shone round me,
      and angels came winging;
   born is our saviour — that is my song.

2 Shepherd-boy, tell me,
   where are you going;
shepherd-boy, tell me, what is your aim?
King in a stable where cattle are lowing:
he is our saviour — that is my aim.

3 Shepherd-boy, tell me,
   why are you kneeling;
shepherd-boy, tell me,
   what is your prayer?
Christ, be my guarding, my saving,
   my healing;
love me, O Saviour — that is my prayer.

117 Traditional, © in this version Word & Music †
Tune: Sandys

1 A child this day is born,
a child of high renown;
most worthy of a sceptre —
a sceptre and a crown.

2 Good news the shepherds heard,
who watched their flock and fold;
the angel that appeared to them
of God's salvation told.

3 The angel host proclaimed
good-will and peace on earth;
for God's redeeming love was shown
in Jesus' holy birth.

4 They praised the Lord our God,
our great celestial King:
now 'Glory in the highest heaven!'
let all creation sing.

5 And what the angel said,
did yet in truth appear;
at Bethlehem they found the child,
laid in a manger there.

6 Then glory be to God
who reigns supreme on high;
with glad thanksgiving, worthy praise,
and joyful melody!

7 Glad tidings sing to all,
glad tidings all shall say,
because the King of all kings
was born on Christmas Day.

118 J Byrom, © in this version Word & Music †
Tune: Yorkshire

1 Christians, awake, salute the happy morn
on which the saviour of the world
      was born;
rise to adore the mystery of love
which hosts of angels chanted from above!
With them the joyful tidings first began
of Mary's infant and our God made man.

2 Then to the watchful shepherds it was told,
who heard the herald angel's voice:
      'Behold,
I bring good tidings of a holy birth
to you and every nation on the earth:
this day has God fulfilled
      the promised word;
this day is born a saviour, Christ the Lord!

3 To Bethlehem these shepherds swiftly run
to see the wonder of God's only Son;
they find with Joseph and the lowly maid,
the new-born saviour in a manger laid.
In human form
   their Shepherd they discern,
and to their flocks, still praising God,
   return.

4 O may we keep and ponder in our mind
God's gracious love
   in saving lost mankind:
trace we his footsteps
   who retrieved our loss,
from his poor manger to his bitter cross.
Saved by his love, unceasing we shall sing
eternal praise to heaven's mighty king!

119 E Caswall, © in this version Jubilate Hymns †
Tune: Humility

1 See, amid the winter snow,
born for us on earth below;
see, the gentle Lamb appears,
promised from eternal years:
   Hail, O ever-blessèd morn;
   hail, redemption's happy dawn!
   Sing through all Jerusalem:
   'Christ is born in Bethlehem!'

2 Low within a manger lies
he who built the starry skies;
he who, throned in height sublime,
reigns above the cherubim:
   Hail, O ever-blessèd morn . . .

3 Say, you humble shepherds, say
what your joyful news today?
tell us why you left your sheep
on the lonely mountain steep:
   Hail, O ever-blessèd morn . . .

4 'As we watched at dead of night,
all around us shone a light;
angels singing Peace on earth
told us of a Saviour's birth.'
   Hail, O ever-blessèd morn . . .

5 Sacred infant, king most dear,
what a tender love was here,
thus to come from highest bliss
down to such a world as this!
   Hail, O ever-blessèd morn . . .

6 Holy saviour, born on earth,
teach us by your lowly birth;
grant that we may ever be
taught by such humility.
   Hail, O ever-blessèd morn;
   hail, redemption's happy dawn!
   Sing through all Jerusalem:
   'Christ is born in Bethlehem!'

7 Now to the Lord sing praises,
all people in this place!
with Christian love and fellowship
each other now embrace,
and let this Christmas festival
all bitterness displace:
   O tidings of comfort and joy . . .

120 Traditional, © in this version Jubilate Hymns †
Tune: God rest you merry

1 God rest you merry, gentlemen,
let nothing you dismay!
for Jesus Christ our saviour
was born on Christmas Day,
to save us all from Satan's power
when we were gone astray:
   O tidings of comfort and joy,
   comfort and joy!
   O tidings of comfort and joy!

2 At Bethlehem in Judah
the holy babe was born;
they laid him in a manger
on this most happy morn:
at which his mother Mary
did neither fear nor scorn:
   O tidings of comfort and joy . . .

3 From God our heavenly Father
a holy angel came;
the shepherds saw the glory
and heard the voice proclaim
that Christ was born in Bethlehem —
and Jesus is his name:
   O tidings of comfort and joy . . .

4 Fear not, then said the angel,
let nothing cause you fright;
to you is born a saviour
in David's town tonight,
to free all those who trust in him
from Satan's power and might:
   O tidings of comfort and joy . . .

5 The shepherds at these tidings
rejoiced in heart and mind,
and on the darkened hillside
they left their flocks behind,
and went to Bethlehem straightway
this holy child to find:
   O tidings of comfort and joy . . .

6 And when to Bethlehem they came
where Christ the infant lay;
they found him in a manger
where oxen fed on hay,
and there beside her newborn child
his mother knelt to pray:
   O tidings of comfort and joy . . .

121 West Indian, © collected Boosey & Hawkes
Tune: The virgin Mary

1 The virgin Mary had a baby boy,
the virgin Mary had a baby boy,
the virgin Mary had a baby boy
and they say that his name is Jesus.
   He come from the glory,
   he come from the glorious kingdom;
   he come from the glory,
   he come from the glorious kingdom:
     O yes, believer!
     O yes, believer!
   He come from the glory,
   he come from the glorious kingdom.

2 The angels sang when the baby was born,
the angels sang when the baby was born,
the angels sang when the baby was born
and they sang that his name is Jesus.
   He come from his glory . . .

3 The shepherds came
   where the baby was born,
the shepherds came
   where the baby was born,
the shepherds came
   where the baby was born
and they say that his name is Jesus.
   He come from the glory . . .

122 © Michael Saward †
Tune: Every star shall sing a carol

1 Christmas for God's holy people
is a time of joy and peace:
so, all Christian men and women,
hymns and carols let us raise
   to our God
   come to earth,
Son of Man, by human birth.

2 Child of Mary, virgin mother,
peasant baby, yet our king,
cradled there among the oxen:
joyful carols now we sing
   to our God . . .

3 Angel armies sang in chorus
at our Christ's nativity,
he who came to share our nature:
so we sing with gaiety
   to our God . . .

4 Shepherds hurried to the manger,
saw the babe in Bethlehem,
glorified the God of heaven:
now we join to sing with them
to our God . . .

5 Infant lowly, born in squalor,
prophet, king and great high priest,
Word of God, to us descending:
still we sing, both great and least,
to our God . . .

123 ©Timothy Dudley-Smith
Tune: Cuxham

1 Stars of heaven, clear and bright,
shine upon this Christmas night.
Vaster far than midnight skies
are its timeless mysteries.
Trampled earth and stable floor
lift the heart to heaven's door —
God has sent to us his Son,
earth and heaven meet as one.

2 Sleepy sounds of beast and byre
mingle with the angel choir.
Highest heaven bends in awe
where he lies amid the straw,
who from light eternal came
aureoled in candle-flame —
God has sent . . .

3 Wide-eyed shepherds mutely gaze
at the child whom angels praise.
Threefold gifts the wise men bring
to the infant priest and king:
to the Lord immortal, myrrh
for an earthly sepulchre —
God has sent . . .

4 Heaven of heavens hails his birth,
King of glory, child of earth,
born in flesh to reign on high,
Prince of life to bleed and die.
Throned on Mary's lap he lies,
Lord of all eternities —
God has sent . . .

5 'Glory be to God on high,
peace on earth,' the angels cry.
Ancient enmities at rest,
ransomed, reconciled and blessed,
in the peace of Christ we come,
come we joyful, come we home —
God has sent . . .

124 © Michael Perry †
Tune: Hayle

1 Jesus, child of Mary born,
Son of God and Lord most high;
come to wear a crown of thorn,
bravely come to die.

2 To this place of pain and fear
love descends in human guise;
God in Christ self-emptied here,
foolishness most wise:

3 Infant in a manger laid,
wrapped about with peasant shawl;
gift of grace so freely made,
saviour for us all.

4 Angel hosts the skies adorn,
we with shepherds glorify
Jesus, child of Mary born,
Son of God most high.

125 © Paul Wigmore †
Tune: Jezus malusienki

1 Such a night in Bethlehem;
such a noise and a rushing!
All the world here,
young and old here,
such a crowd and a crushing!
God is with us, God is with us;
Christ the Lord is our saviour!

2 Such a light on Bethlehem;
such a glare and a blazing!
Angels winging,
heaven singing,
shepherds fearfully gazing!
God is with us . . .

3 Such a sight in Bethlehem;
such a king in a manger!
God above us
come to love us
with the poor and the stranger!
God is with us . . .

126/127 From the Danish, © Michael Perry †
Tunes: A child is born, Sing nowell

1 A child is born in Bethlehem,
Sing nowell (sing nowell)!
the royal flower to David's stem.
Alleluia, alleluia!

2 Sing praises through the whole wide earth,
Sing nowell (sing nowell)!
for Mary gives the Saviour birth.
Alleluia, alleluia!

3 He lies within a manger bare,
Sing nowell (sing nowell)!
and shepherds kneel to worship there.
Alleluia, alleluia!

4 He comes to be our hope of peace,
Sing nowell (sing nowell)!
to bring imprisoned souls release.
Alleluia, alleluia!

5 Our guilt has found a certain cure,
Sing nowell (sing nowell)!
for Christ makes our salvation sure.
Alleluia, alleluia!

128
From the Latin, © Michael Perry †
Tune: Personent hodie

1 Shout aloud, girls and boys!
Sing today and rejoice,
lift your heart, raise your voice;
come, and do not waver,
God has shown us favour:
  virgin-born, born, born,
  virgin-born, born, born,
virgin-born, Mary's child,
  Christ is here — our saviour!

2 There you lie, Lord of all!
For your robe — peasant shawl,
for your bed — ox's stall,
for your throne a manger,
homeless as a stranger;
  come to win, win, win,
  come to win, win, win,
come to win hell's domain —
  spurning death and danger!

3 Even now, from afar
wise men seek heaven's star,
bringing gifts where you are:
gold to bow before you,
incense to implore you,
  myrrh to say, say, say,
  myrrh to say, say, say,
myrrh to say 'sacrifice' —
  therefore we adore you!

4 Boys and girls, voices raise!
Christmas choirs, sweetly phrase
songs of joy and of praise;
leave all care and worry,
sing the angels' story:
  Christ is born, born, born;
  Christ is born, born, born,
Christ is born, Peace on earth —
  and to God be glory!

129
© Michael Perry †
Tune: Past three a clock

  Ring out the bells —
  the joyful news is breaking;
  ring out the bells
  for Jesus Christ is born!

1 Angels in wonder
  sing of his glory;
shepherds returning
  tell us the story.
  Ring out . . .

2 Let all creation
  worship before him:
earth bring him homage,
  heaven adore him!
  Ring out . . .

3 Prophets have spoken —
  hark to their warning:
shadows are passing,
  soon comes the morning!
  Ring out . . .

130
After German authors, © Michael Perry †
Tune: Puer nobis

1 Jesus Christ the Lord is born,
all the bells are ringing!
angels greet the holy One
  and shepherds hear them singing,
  and shepherds hear them singing:

2 'Go to Bethlehem today,
find your king and saviour:
glory be to God on high,
  to earth his peace and favour,
  to earth his peace and favour!'

3 Held within a cattle stall,
loved by love maternal,
see the master of us all,
  our Lord of lords eternal,
  our Lord of lords eternal!

4 Soon shall come the wise men three,
rousing Herod's anger;
mothers' hearts shall broken be
  and Mary's son in danger,
  and Mary's son in danger.

5 Death from life and life from death,
our salvation's story:
let all living things give breath
  to Christmas songs of glory,
  to Christmas songs of glory!

131/132
C Smart
Tunes: Lismore, Kit Smart

1 Where is this stupendous stranger?
prophets, shepherds, kings, advise:
lead me to my Master's manger,
show me where my Saviour lies.

2 O most Mighty, O most Holy,
far beyond the seraph's thought,
are you then so poor and lowly
as unheeded prophets taught?

3 O the magnitude of meekness,
worth from Worth immortal sprung;
O the strength of infant weakness,
if the eternal is so young!

4 God all-gracious, all-creative,
whom no wrongs from good dissuade,
is incarnate — and a native
of the very world he made.

133
W C Dix, © in this version Word & Music †
Tune: Greensleeves

1 What Child is this who, laid to rest
on Mary's lap, is sleeping;
whom angels greet with anthems sweet,
while shepherds watch are keeping?
  This, this is Christ the king,
  whom shepherds seek and angels sing:
  haste, haste to bring him praise,
  the babe, the son of Mary.

2 Why lies he in so poor a place,
  where ox and ass are feeding?
  Good Christians, fear — for God is here,
  and for our peace is pleading.
    This, this . . .

3 So bring him incense, gold and myrrh,
  come humbly to revere him:
  the King of kings salvation brings —
  let faithful hearts draw near him.
    This, this . . .

134 After Prudentius, © Michael Perry †
Tune: Stuttgart

1 Bethlehem, what greater city
  can in fame with you compare?
  For the gracious God of heaven
  chose to meet his people there.

2 Was there ever beauty brighter
  than the star which shone that night
  to proclaim the incarnation
  of our God, the world's true light?

3 From the East come men of learning:
  rich the treasures that they hold —
  tributes to a greater wisdom,
  gifts of incense, myrrh and gold.

4 Sacrifice, redeemer, saviour!
  Incense shows that God has come,
  gold, our mighty king, proclaims him,
  myrrh foretells his silent tomb.

5 Jesus Christ, to you be glory,
  Lord of lords whom we adore:
  Father, Son and Holy Spirit —
  God be praised for evermore!

135 After J A Schlegel, C Winkworth
© in this version Word & Music †
Tune: Wie schön leuchtet

1 How brightly gleams the morning star!
  What sudden radiance from afar
  delights us with its shining?
  God's glory breaks upon the night,
  and fills our darkened souls with light,
  who long for truth were pining!
    Your word, Jesus,
    truly feeds us,
    rightly leads us,
    life bestowing.
  Praise such mercy overflowing!

2 By you alone can we be blessed —
  then deep be on our hearts impressed
  the love that you have borne us;
  so make us ready to fulfil
  with fervent zeal your holy will,
  though many vex or scorn us.

Saviour, let us
gladly hear you,
duly fear you,
long to know you!
All we are and have, we owe you.

3 All praise to him who comes to save,
  who conquered death
    and spurned the grave!
  Our adoration rises
  to him, the Lamb who once was slain,
  the Friend whom none shall trust in vain,
  whose mercy yet surprises.
    Sing, you heavens,
    tell the story
    of his glory,
    till his praises
  flood with light earth's darkest places!

136A After P Cornelius and J A Schlegel, H N Bate
© Oxford University Press
and in this version Word & Music †
Tune: The Three Kings

1 Three kings from Persian lands afar
  to Jordan follow the pointing star;
  and this the quest of the travellers three,
  where the new-born king of the Jews
    may be;
  full royal gifts they bear for the king —
  gold, incense, myrrh are their offering.

2 The star shines out with a steadfast ray,
  the kings to Bethlehem make their way,
  and there in worship they bend the knee,
  as Mary's child in her lap they see;
  their royal gifts they show to the king —
  gold, incense, myrrh are their offering.

3 O child of man, go to Bethlehem,
  the kings are travelling — travel with them!
  The star of mercy, the star of grace,
  shall lead your heart to its resting place.
  Gold, incense, myrrh you cannot bring:
  offer your heart to the infant king,

  offer your heart!

136B After P Cornelius and J A Schlegel, H N Bate
© Oxford University Press
and in this version Word & Music †
Tune: Wie schön leuchtet

1 How brightly shines the morning star
  with grace and truth from heaven afar!
  The promised tree is growing
  from Jacob's root through David's line:
  you come, O Bridegroom, King divine,
  with love beyond all knowing.
    Your word, Jesus,
    truly feeds us,
    rightly leads us,
    life bestowing.
  Praise such mercy overflowing!

137 © Paul Wigmore †
Tune: Infinite Light

1 Bright mystical starlight
    shone over the place
where Jesus our saviour
    first showed us his face;
his sweet mother Mary
    watched over the stall
where God, now incarnate,
    first welcomed us all:
The starlight, the shepherds,
    the angels and kings,
all tell us of Christ
    and the joy that he brings.

2 The Bethlehem shepherds
    were keeping their sheep,
not caring for comfort, not daring to sleep;
then out of the starlight
    came news of great joy,
for God is incarnate, and born as a boy:
The starlight . . .

3 The angels were filling
    that Bethlehem night,
the air with their song
    and the hills with their light;
the message they sang
    is for you and for me —
our God is incarnate, and setting us free:
The starlight . . .

4 Three wise men and noble
    came out of the east,
they came to the town
    that of all was the least;
they followed the starlight
    and came to the king,
our God, now incarnate,
    who hears as we sing:
The starlight . . .

138 From the Swedish, © Paul Wigmore †
Tune: I himmelen, i himmelen

1 The star of heaven foretells the joy
that we in heaven shall know;
to see you, Lord God, face to face
and walk where angels go!
And in that land of holy light
no guilt of sin, no dread of night,
    O Lord of earth and heaven!

2 So bright the star! We see it shine
your heavenly light on earth:
how pure the light of God come down
in joy of human birth!
And brighter than the morning sun
is Jesus Christ, your holy One,
    O Lord of earth and heaven!

139 J H Hopkins
Tune: Kings of Orient

1 ALL
We three kings of orient are,
bearing gifts we travel afar —
field and fountain, moor and mountain —
following yonder star,
    O star of wonder, star of night,
    star with royal beauty bright:
    westward leading, still proceeding,
    guide us to your perfect light!

2 FIRST
Born a king on Bethlehem's plain —
gold I bring to crown him again:
king for ever, ceasing never,
over us all to reign.
    ALL O star of wonder . . .

3 SECOND
Frankincense to offer have I —
incense tells of Deity nigh;
prayer and praising all are raising:
worship him — God most high!
    ALL O star of wonder . . .

4 THIRD
Myrrh is mine — its bitter perfume
breathes a life of gathering gloom:
sorrowing, sighing, bleeding, dying,
sealed in the stone-cold tomb.
    ALL O star of wonder . . .

5 ALL
Glorious now behold him arise —
king and God and sacrifice!
Heaven sings 'Alleluia!' —
'Alleluia!' the earth replies.
    O star of wonder . . .

140 R Heber, © in this version Jubilate Hymns †
Tune: Epiphany Hymn

1 Brightest and best
    of the sons of the morning,
dawn on our darkness and come to our aid;
star of the east, the horizon adorning,
guide where our infant redeemer is laid!

2 What shall we give him, in costly devotion?
Shall we bring incense
    and offerings divine,
gems of the mountain
    and pearls of the ocean,
myrrh from the forest
    or gold from the mine?

3 Vainly we offer each lavish oblation,
vainly with gifts would his favour secure;
richer by far is the heart's adoration,
dearer to God are the prayers of the poor.

4 Brightest and best
   of the sons of the morning,
dawn on our darkness and come to our aid;
star of the east, the horizon adorning,
guide where our infant redeemer is laid!

141 Traditional, © in this version Word & Music †
Tune: Gallery Carol

1 Rejoice and be merry
   in songs and in mirth;
O praise our redeemer,
   all mortals on earth!
for this is the birthday of Jesus our king,
who brought us salvation —
his praises we'll sing!

2 A heavenly vision appeared in the sky;
vast numbers of angels
   the shepherds did spy,
proclaiming the birthday of Jesus our king,
who brought us salvation —
his praises we'll sing!

3 And soon in the sky
   a bright star did appear,
which led the wise men from the east
   to draw near;
they found the messiah,
   Christ Jesus our king,
who brought us salvation —
his praises we'll sing!

4 They came and they offered
   myrrh, incense and gold —
for God's gracious purpose
   these treasures foretold:
then worshipped for ever
   be Jesus our king,
who brought us salvation —
his praises we'll sing!

142 Unknown, © in this version Word & Music †
Tune: The first nowell

1 The first nowell the angel did say,
   was to Bethlehem's shepherds
      in fields as they lay;
in fields where they
      lay keeping their sheep
on a cold winter's night that was so deep:
   Nowell, nowell, nowell, nowell,
   born is the king of Israel!

2 Then wise men from a country far
looked up and saw a guiding star;
they travelled on by night and day
to reach the place where Jesus lay:
   Nowell, nowell . . .

3 At Bethlehem they entered in,
on bended knee they worshipped him;
they offered there in his presence
their gold and myrrh and frankincense:
   Nowell, nowell . . .

4 Then let us all with one accord
sing praises to our heavenly Lord;
for Christ has our salvation wrought
and with his blood mankind has bought:
   Nowell, nowell . . .

143 © Paul Wigmore †
Tune: Noël nouvelet

1 Mary came with meekness,
   Jesus Christ to bear,
laid the Lord of glory
   in a manger there.
      We come rejoicing,
      Jesus Christ to love:
   baby in a manger —
   king of heaven above!

2 Angels came with praises,
   Jesus Christ to name,
heaven's choirs exalting
   him who bears our shame.
      We come rejoicing . . .

3 Shepherds came with trembling,
   Jesus Christ to see;
king who, at their bidding,
   would their shepherd be.
      We come rejoicing . . .

4 Wise men came with treasure,
   Jesus Christ to bless —
he who shares all blessings
heaven and earth possess.
      We come rejoicing . . .

144 From the Polish, John Rutter
© Oxford University Press
Tune: The coming of our king

1 Hark! do you hear
      how the angel voices sing,
   bearing the news
      of the coming of our King?
Hark! do you hear . . .
      Jesus Christ is born to save us:
      Satan's power shall not enslave us!
Hark! do you hear . . .

2 Hush! for the baby lies sleeping in the hay,
cradled at Bethlehem very far away.
Hush! for the baby . . .
      Ox and ass before him kneeling,
      Mary's love his sorrows healing.
Hush! for the baby . . .

3 See! now a star shining in the eastern skies,
guiding the wise men
      to where in infant lies.
See! now a star . . .
      Gifts they bring of richest treasure,
      offer homage without measure.
See! now a star . . .

4 Come! with the wise men
　　your faithful homage pay,
　sing and rejoice
　　　that our Lord is born today.
　Come: with the wise men . . .
　　Greet the child with shouts of gladness:
　　banish sorrow, banish sadness!
　Come! with the wise men . . .

145 From the Dutch, © Paul Wigmore†
Tune: Nu zijt wellekome

1 Jesus, you are welcome
　　Jesus, our dear Lord;
　from home in farthest heaven
　　　you come, adored.
　Life on earth so brief beginning,
　　Christ, eternal Word!
　From the bells of heaven
　　what welcoming is poured!
　Have mercy, Lord.

2 Shepherds on the hillside
　　hear the angels' song;
　it tells them of a Saviour
　　　awaited long:
　'Go along the streets to find him,
　　down among the throng,
　baby born of Mary
　　to save us from all wrong.'
　Have mercy, Lord.

3 Wise men in the dawn-light
　　come with eastern gold,
　with sweetest myrrh and incense
　　　for Christ to hold.
　Bowed before the holy child
　　they see him long foretold,
　Jesus Christ who makes us
　　all welcome in his fold.
　Have mercy, Lord.

146 W C Dix, © in this version Word & Music †
Tune: Dix

1 As with gladness men of old
　did the guiding star behold,
　as with joy they hailed its light,
　leading onward, gleaming bright:
　so, most gracious Lord, may we
　evermore your splendour see.

2 As with joyful steps they sped
　to that lowly manger bed,
　there to bend the knee before
　Christ whom heaven and earth adore:
　so with ever-quickening pace
　may we seek your throne of grace.

3 As they offered gifts most rare
　at your cradle plain and bare,
　so may we with holy joy
　pure and free from sin's alloy,
　all our costliest treasures bring,
　Christ, to you, our heavenly king.

4 Holy Jesus, every day
　keep us in the narrow way,
　and when earthly things are past,
　bring our ransomed souls at last:
　where they need no star to guide,
　where no clouds your glory hide.

5 In the heavenly country bright
　none shall need created light —
　Christ its light, its joy, its crown,
　Christ its sun which goes not down:
　there for ever may we sing
　alleluias to our king.

147 From the Latin, G B Caird, © Mrs V Caird
Tune: Quem pastores laudavere

1 Shepherds came, their praises bringing,
　who had heard the angels singing:
　'Far from you be fear unruly,
　Christ is king of glory born.'

2 Wise men whom a star had guided
　incense, gold, and myrrh provided,
　made their sacrifices truly
　to the king of glory born.

3 Jesus born the king of heaven,
　Christ to us through Mary given,
　to your praise and honour duly
　be resounding glory done.

148/149 © Paul Wigmore †
Tune: No small wonder

1 Small wonder the star,
　　small wonder the light,
　the angels in chorus,
　　the shepherds in fright;
　but stable and manger for God —
　no small wonder!

2 Small wonder the kings,
　　small wonder they bore
　the gold and the incense,
　　the myrrh, to adore;
　but God gives his life on a cross —
　no small wonder!

3 Small wonder the love,
　　small wonder the grace,
　the power, the glory,
　　the light of his face;
　but all to redeem my poor heart —
　no small wonder!

150 J B Monsell
Tune: Was lebet

1 O worship the Lord
    in the beauty of holiness,
    bow down before him,
        his glory proclaim;
    with gold of obedience
        and incense of lowliness,
    kneel and adore him —
        the Lord is his name.

2 Low at his feet
        lay your burden of carefulness,
    high on his heart
        he will bear it for you,
    comfort your sorrows
        and answer your prayerfulness,
    guiding your steps
        in the way that is true.

3 Fear not to enter his courts
        in the slenderness
    of the poor wealth
        you would count as your own;
    truth in its beauty
        and love in its tenderness —
    these are the offerings
        to bring to his throne.

4 These, though we bring them
        in trembling and fearfulness,
    he will accept
        for the name that is dear;
    mornings of joy give
        for evenings of tearfulness,
    trust for our trembling
        and hope for our fear.

5 O worship the Lord
    in the beauty of holiness,
    bow down before him,
        his glory proclaim;
    with gold of obedience
        and incense of lowliness,
    kneel and adore him —
        the Lord is his name.

151 After H Berlioz, © Paul Wigmore †
Tune: The Shepherds' Farewell

1 Jesus, child of gentle Mary,
    as now you leave your lowly bed,
    hear the shepherds' prayer of blessing,
    for danger stalks the path you tread:
    Mary hold you, Joseph lead you,
    God be ever at your head;
    Mary hold you . . .

    God be ever at your head.

2 When you walk among the heathen
    and suffer torment, grief and pain,
    shepherds in their joy implore you,
    return to Bethlehem again!

Let the poor, the weak and humble
in your heart of love remain;
let the poor . . .

In your heart of love remain.

3 Though the clouds of evil hover,
    though winds of cold injustice blow,
    angels of the Lord surround you,
    protect you, guide you here below;
    holy child of human mother,
    God be with you as you go;
    holy child . . .

    God be with you as you go!

152 R Croo, © in this version Word & Music †
Tune: Coventry Carol
*The refrain may be omitted, or sung here only

    *Hush, do not cry,
        my little tiny child:
    Lullaby, lullalay!

1 O brothers, tell
    what ill befell
    Bethlehem's town this day;
    let grief recite
    these infants' plight,
    sorrow and sore dismay.
        Hush, do not cry . . .

2 O sisters too,
    what may we do
    and save from death today
    this poor young thing
    to whom we sing:
    'Lullaby, lullalay'?
        Hush, do not cry . . .

3 Herod the king,
    in his raging,
    gave his command this day:
    his men of might
    in his own sight
    all little boys to slay.
        Hush, do not cry . . .

4 Then woe is me,
    poor child, to see
    this sad and sorry day;
    from your parting
    we say nor sing,
    'Lullaby, lullalay.'
        Hush, do not cry . . .

153 Brian Wren, © Oxford University Press
Tune: Christmas Now

1 Child, when Herod wakes,
    and hate or exploitation
    swing their dripping swords,
    from your cross and cradle
    sing a new song.

2 Child, when Caesar's laws
choke love or strangle freedom,
calling darkness light,
from your cross and cradle
sing a new song.

3 Child, when Caiaphas
sends truth to crucifixion
to protect his prayers,
from your cross and cradle
sing a new song.

4 Child, your helpless love
brings death and resurrection:
joyfully we come
to your cross and cradle
with a new song —
Alleluia, alleluia!

154 From Luke 2 — *The Song of Simeon/*
Nunc Dimittis, © Timothy Dudley-Smith
Tune: Faithful vigil

1 Faithful vigil ended,
watching, waiting cease:
Master, grant your servant
his discharge in peace.

2 All the Spirit promised,
all the Father willed,
now these eyes behold it
perfectly fulfilled.

3 This your great deliverance
sets your people free;
Christ their light uplifted
all the nations see.

4 Christ, your people's glory!
watching, doubting cease;
grant to us your servants
our discharge in peace.

155 © Kenneth G Hockridge
Tune: Zu Bethlehem geboren

1 The Lord of life and glory
came down on earth to dwell,
and angels hailed his coming,
our Lord Emmanuel:
    God with us, God with us,
    our Lord Emmanuel!

2 But Bethlehem of Judah
despised a king so poor;
no inn, no house was open
to him who is the Door:
    God with us . . .

3 A virgin bore a baby,
in flesh God manifest;
the mighty God, the Prince of peace
found in a manger rest:
    God with us . . .

4 The wise men and the shepherds
to Jesus made their way;
to bring their gifts of honour
and in their worship say:
    'God with us . . .'

5 Since Simeon in the temple
held Christ in loving hands,
and Anna saw the saviour,
his praise has reached all lands:
    God with us . . .

6 So let us praise our saviour,
lift up our hearts and sing
of Christ who came to save us
and lives to be our king:
    God with us . . .

156/157 From Luke 2 — *The Song of*
Simeon/Nunc Dimittis
J E Seddon, © Mrs M Seddon †
Tunes: North Coates, Caswall

1 Lord, now let your servant
go his way in peace;
your great love has brought me
joy that will not cease:

2 For my eyes have seen him
promised from of old —
saviour of all people,
shepherd of one fold:

3 Light of revelation
to the gentiles shown,
light of Israel's glory
to the world made known.

158 © David Mowbray †
Tune: Child of mine

1 Child of mine, the Virgin sings,
child of mine, yet King of kings;
promised us by Gabriel,
Jesus Christ, Emmanuel.

2 Child of mine — how can this be?
Child of mine — what mystery!
But things are as God has planned,
all are safe within his hand.

3 Child of mine and gift from heaven;
child of mine that God has given.
Firstborn son, and precious boy,
born to sorrow, born to joy.

4 Child of mine, soon sorrow's dart,
child of mine, shall pierce my heart;
but great joy is rising there,
joy for all the world to share.

5 Child of mine — among us now,
Jesus Christ, come show us how
Love has come to drive out fear:
all are blessed, for God is here!

159 Traditional, © in this version Word & Music †
Tune: The holly and the ivy

1 The holly and the ivy
   when they are both full grown —
   of all the trees that are in the wood,
   the holly bears the crown.
     Oh, the rising of the sun
     and the running of the deer,
     the playing of the merry organ,
     sweet singing in the choir!

2 The holly bears a blossom
   as white as any flower;
   and Mary bore sweet Jesus Christ
   to be our true saviour.
     Oh, the rising . . .

3 The holly bears a berry
   as red as any blood;
   and Mary bore sweet Jesus Christ
   to die for all our good.
     Oh, the rising . . .

4 The holly bears a prickle,
   as sharp as any thorn;
   and Mary bore sweet Jesus Christ
   to wear a cruel crown.
     Oh, the rising . . .

5 The holly bears a bark
   as bitter as any gall;
   and Mary bore sweet Jesus Christ
   to suffer for us all.
     Oh, the rising . . .

6 The holly and the ivy
   when they are both full grown —
   of all the trees that are in the wood,
   the holly bears the crown.
     Oh, the rising . . .

160 J Chandler, © in this version Word & Music †
Tune: Winchester New

1 On Jordan's bank the Baptist's cry
   announces that the Lord is nigh:
   awake and listen for he brings
   glad tidings of the King of kings.

2 Let every heart be cleansed from sin,
   make straight the way for God within,
   and so prepare to be the home
   where such a mighty guest may come.

3 For you are our salvation, Lord,
   our refuge and our great reward;
   without your grace we waste away
   like flowers that wither and decay.

4 To heal the sick, stretch out your hand,
   and make the fallen sinner stand;
   shine out, and let your light restore
   earth's own true loveliness once more.

5 To you, O Christ, all praises be,
   whose advent sets your people free;
   whom with the Father we adore
   and Holy Spirit evermore!

161/162 C Wordsworth
© in this version Jubilate Hymns †
Tunes: St Edmund, St George's Windsor

1 Songs of thankfulness and praise,
   Jesus, Lord, to you we raise;
   once revealed, when heaven's star
   brought the wise men from afar;
   branch of royal David's stem
   in your birth at Bethlehem,
     Word before the world began,
     God revealed to us in man.

2 God revealed at Jordan's stream,
   prophet, priest and king supreme;
   once revealed in power divine
   changing water into wine;
   Cana's holy wedding guest
   keeping to the last the best;
     Word before the world began . . .

3 God revealed in valiant fight,
   conquering the devil's might;
   sins forgiven, sickness healed,
   life restored and God revealed:
   once revealed in gracious will
   ever bringing good from ill,
     Word before the world began . . .

4 Stars shall fall and heavens fade,
   sun and moon shall dark be made;
   Christ will then like lightning shine,
   all will see the glorious sign;
   all will then the trumpet hear,
   all will see the Son appear,
     Word before the world began . . .

163 © David Mowbray †
Tune: Bergers

1 Word of the Father everlasting,
   there at his side when time began;
   who but the Word reflects his glory,
   who but the Word may speak to man?
     Word of the Father everlasting,
     there at his side when time began.

2 Word once made flesh
     in Mary's keeping,
   source of all life and one true light;
   who of his own will dare receive him,
   or to their homes and hearts invite?
     Word once made flesh
       in Mary's keeping,
     source of all life and one true light.

3 Word full of grace, among us dwelling,
   Jesus our Lord, the Father's Son:
   give us the power,
     your name confessing,
   truly God's children to become.
     Word full of grace,
       among us dwelling,
     Jesus our Lord, the Father's Son.

164/165

C Rossetti
© in this version Jubilee Hymns †
Tunes: Gartan, Hermitage

1 Love came down at Christmas,
love all lovely, love divine;
love was born at Christmas —
star and angels gave the sign.

2 Worship we the Godhead,
love incarnate, love divine;
worship we our Jesus —
what shall be our sacred sign?

3 Love shall be our token,
love be yours and love be mine;
love to God and neighbour,
love for prayer and gift and sign.

166

© Timothy Dudley-Smith
Tune: Beacon Hill

1 Had he not loved us
he had never come,
yet is he love
and love is all his way;
low to the mystery
of the virgin's womb
Christ bows his glory —
born on Christmas Day.

2 Had he not loved us
he had never come;
had he not come
he need have never died,
nor won the victory
of the vacant tomb,
the awful triumph
of the crucified.

3 Had he not loved us
he had never come;
still were we lost
in sorrow, sin and shame,
the doors fast shut
on our eternal home
which now stand open —
for he loved and came.

167

© Timothy Dudley-Smith
Tune: He comes to us

1 He comes to us as one unknown,
a breath unseen, unheard;
as though within a heart of stone,
or shrivelled seed in darkness sown,
a pulse of being stirred.

2 He comes when souls in silence lie
and thoughts of day depart;
half seen upon the inward eye,
a falling star across the sky
of night within the heart.

3 He comes to us in sound of seas,
the ocean's fume and foam;
yet small and still upon the breeze,
a wind that stirs the tops of trees,
a voice to call us home.

4 He comes in love as once he came
by flesh and blood and birth;
to bear within our mortal frame
a life, a death, a saving Name,
for every child of earth.

5 He comes in truth when faith is grown;
believed, obeyed, adored:
the Christ in all the Scriptures shown,
as yet unseen, but not unknown,
our Saviour and our Lord.

168

B Rees, © Mrs M Rees
Tune: Jesus is born

1 The God we seek, beyond all thought,
has now his Christmas wonder wrought:
behold, the seeker is the sought!
Waiting ended,
man befriended:
Jesus is born:

2 Love is the manger where he lies,
love is the cross on which he dies;
stronger than death shall love arise:
Glorious meekness,
power in weakness:
Jesus is born.

3 Into the love of Christ the king
our lives, our world, in faith we bring:
the sin, the pain, the suffering.
God esteems us,
Christ redeems us:
Jesus is born!

169

Appalachian Carol
© in this version Word & Music †
Tune: I wonder as I wander

1 I wonder as I wander,
out under the sky,
why Jesus the saviour
came down from on high
for us lowly people
to suffer and die —
I wonder as I wander,
out under the sky.

2 When Jesus was born —
it was in a cow's stall —
came angels and shepherds
and wise men and all,
and from the high heaven
a star's light did fall,
the wonderful promise of God
to recall.

3 If Jesus had wanted
    for any one thing —
a star in the sky,
    or a bird on the wing,
or all of God's angels in heaven
    to sing —
he surely could have it,
    for he was the king.

4 I wonder as I wander,
    out under the sky,
why Jesus the saviour
    came down from on high
for us lowly people
    to suffer and die —
I wonder as I wander,
    out under the sky.

170 From the German, J Troutbeck
Tune: from *Christmas Oratorio*

Rejoice and sing, rejoice and sing!
Your gracious king as man is born
    and lays aside his glory;
he is adored as Christ the Lord,
and every tongue repeats
    the wondrous story.

171/172 From Philippians 2 —
The Song of Christ's Glory
© Brian Black † and Word & Music †
Tunes: Munden, Narenza

1 Before the heaven and earth
were made by God's decree,
the Son of God all-glorious dwelt
in God's eternity.

2 Though in the form of God
and rich beyond compare,
he did not stay to grasp his prize;
nor did he linger there.

3 From heights of heaven he came
to this world full of sin,
to meet with hunger, hatred, hell,
our life, our love to win.

4 The Son became true Man
and took a servant's role;
with lowliness and selfless love
he came, to make us whole.

5 Obedient to his death —
that death upon a cross,
no son had ever shown such love,
nor father known such loss.

6 To him enthroned on high,
by angel hosts adored,
all knees shall bow, and tongues confess
that Jesus Christ is Lord.

173/174 From Philippians 2 —
The Song of Christ's Glory
© Michael Perry †
Tunes: Purpose, Slane

1 Down from the height of his glory he came,
willingly leaving his rightful domain:
Jesus was born in the image of man,
love was his motive and mercy his aim.

2 All through those days
    his resolve was the same —
Jesus the servant, the sharer of pain:
perfect obedience, the path of disdain,
down to a death of derision and shame.

3 Now God has granted him
    honour and fame,
taken him up to the highest to reign:
'Jesus is Lord!' every voice shall maintain,
all of creation shall bow to his name.

175/176 T Pestel
© in this version Jubilate Hymns †
Tunes: Kilmarnock, This endris nyght

1 Behold, the great Creator makes
himself a house of clay;
a robe of human form he takes
for ever from this day.

2 Hear this! — the wise eternal Word
as Mary's infant cries;
a servant is our mighty Lord,
and God in cradle lies.

3 Glad shepherds run to view this sight,
a choir of angels sings;
wise men from far with pure delight
adore the King of kings.

4 These wonders all the world amaze
and shake the starry frame;
the host of heaven stand to gaze,
and bless the Saviour's name.

5 Join then, all hearts that are not stone,
and all our voices prove
to celebrate the holy One,
the God of peace and love.

177 J M Neale, © in this version Word & Music †
Tune: Tempus adest floridum

1 ALL
Good king Wenceslas looked out
on the Feast of Stephen,
when the snow lay round about,
deep, and crisp, and even:
brightly shone the moon that night,
though the frost was cruel,
when a poor man came in sight,
gathering winter fuel.

2 KING
'Hither, page, and stand by me!
if thou know'st it, telling.
Yonder poor man — who is he,
where and what his dwelling?'
PAGE
'Sire, he lives a good league hence,
underneath the moutain;
right against the forest fence
by Saint Agnes' fountain.'

3 KING
'Bring me flesh, and bring me wine,
bring me pine logs hither:
thou and I will see him dine,
when we bear them thither.'
ALL
Page and monarch forth they went,
forth they went together,
through the wild wind's loud lament,
and the bitter weather.

4 PAGE
'Sire, the night is darker now,
and the wind blows stronger;
fails my heart, I know not how —
I can go no longer.'
KING
'Mark my footsteps, good my page,
tread thou in them boldly:
thou shalt find the winter's rage
freeze thy blood less coldly.'

5 ALL
In his master's steps he trod
where the snow lay even,
strong to do the will of God
in the hope of heaven:
therefore, Christians all, be sure,
grace and wealth possessing,
ye who now will bless the poor
shall yourselves find blessing.

178 © Timothy Dudley-Smith
Tune: Holy Apostles

1 A song was heard at Christmas
to wake the midnight sky;
a saviour's birth, and peace on earth,
and praise to God on high.
The angels sang at Christmas
with all the hosts above,
and still we sing the newborn King,
his glory and his love.

2 A star was seen at Christmas,
a herald and a sign,
that all might know the way to go
to find the child divine.
The wise men watched at Christmas
in some far eastern land,
and still the wise in starry skies
discern their Maker's hand.

3 A tree was grown at Christmas,
a sapling green and young;
no tinsel bright with candlelight
upon its branches hung.
But he who came at Christmas
our sins and sorrows bore,
and still we name his tree of shame
our life for evermore.

4 A child was born at Christmas
when Christmas first began;
the Lord of all a baby small,
the Son of God made man.
For love is ours at Christmas,
and life and light restored,
and so we praise through endless days
the Saviour, Christ the Lord.

179 After J B de Santeuil, R Campbell
© in this version Word & Music †
Tune: Venice

1 How joyful is the song
that tells of peace and love;
of Christ, the Lord awaited long,
descending from above!

2 From God's eternal home
he stooped to time and space,
and humbly chose a virgin's womb
to be his dwelling-place.

3 He lived with us on earth,
by fierce compassion driven,
his life as humble as his birth,
to show the way to heaven,

4 And lowlier, in the tomb
he did not scorn to lie,
that we frail mortals might assume
his immortality.

5 How joyful is the song
that tells of peace and love;
of Christ, the Lord awaited long,
descending from above!

180 Traditional, © in this version Word & Music †
Tune: O Babe divine

1 O Babe divine, to you we sing
a Christmas song of love-longing:
now make our hearts a fervent spring
to love you more than everything.

2 O holy Child, O sight supreme,
our present song, our future theme:
as you were born in Bethlehem,
be born in us and be our dream.

3 O Prince of peace, our dark world's light,
the dawn of day, the end of night:
now give us strength to win the fight —
to conquer sin and live aright.

4 O kingly Christ, our Lord confessed,
   prepare your church to love you best;
   to live and serve at your behest
   in north and south and east and west.

5 O Saviour Jesus, grant us too
   the proof of grace, the heavenly view;
   come, fill our hearts with love anew
   that we may rise to live with you!

181 From the Latin, J M Neale and P Dearmer
Tune: Quem pastores laudavere

1 Jesus, good above all other,
   gentle child of gentle mother;
   in a stable born our brother,
   whom the angel hosts adore:

2 Jesus, cradled in a manger,
   keep us free from sin and danger;
   and to all, both friend and stranger,
   give your blessing evermore.

3 Jesus, for your people dying,
   risen master, death defying;
   Lord of heaven, your grace supplying,
   come to us — be present here!

4 Lord, in all our doings guide us:
   pride and hate shall not divide us;
   we'll go on with you beside us,
   and with joy we'll persevere.

182 © Alan Gaunt
Tune: Joelle

1 Thank you God, for Mary's child
   coming like the rising sun,
   with new promise and fresh hope
   chorusing his matchless dawn.

2 Thank you, God, for each new birth:
   each new person in our hands,
   whose dependence speaks for you,
   reasserts your love's demands.

3 God forgive us — we have made
   such a chaos of the earth
   that anxiety and fear
   mar the miracle of birth.

4 God, forgive our Babel sounds,
   lust for power, religious strife,
   breaking fellowship and peace,
   sapping all the joy of life.

5 Speak to us in every child,
   teach us true humility;
   keep our hope alive, sustain
   love for all humanity:

6 Till in resurrection light,
   peace restored and conflict stilled,
   Christ will rise and shine for us,
   all his promises fulfilled.

183 Brian Wren, © Oxford University Press
Tune: Joseph's Carol

1 You were a child of mine:
   I watched you born, and wept
   with joy to see your infant head;
   I held you in my arms,
   I watched you, awe-struck, as you slept.
      I love you, Son of God:
      you were a child of mine.

2 You were a boy of mine:
   you wallowed in the sand;
   you copied me at work, and played
   with hammer, wood and nails;
   you talked to me, and held my hand.
      I love you, Son of God:
      you were a boy of mine.

3 You were a youth of mine:
   quite suddenly you grew,
   you sought and questioned wiser men;
   I felt you breaking free —
   I raged, admired, and feared for you.
      I love you, Son of God:
      you were a youth of mine.

4 You were a son of mine,
   full-grown, my hope and pride;
   you went your puzzling way, a man
   so ready, fine and young —
   life broke in me the day you died.
      I love you, Son of God:
      you were a son of mine.

5 You are the Lord of all —
   my child, my man, my son;
   you loved and gave yourself for me.
   Now I belong to you;
   new worlds are born, new life begun.
      I love you, Son of God:
      you are the Lord of all.

184 © Paul Wigmore †
Tune: Colwall

1 No frightened shepherds now
   to stand amazed and quake with fear;
   but we, surprised by joy,
   come willingly to Jesus here.

2 No wooden manger-bed,
   where we may kneel in silent awe;
   yet now we kneel in faith
   and see, by faith, what angels saw.

3 No choirs of angels now
   to fill a starlit Christmas sky;
   yet, East to West, there rings
   the worship of the Lord most high.

4 No eastern magi here,
   no gold or frankincense or myrrh;
   yet each as precious now
   these hearts of ours as gifts that were.

ADVENT PRAYER

ACT OF PRAISE
(AT HOLY COMMUNION)

Jesus, you come to live among us, born
of the virgin Mary. We give you thanks:
and praise your holy name.

Jesus, you come to us as we read your
story in the Bible. We give you thanks:
and praise your holy name.

Jesus, you come to us as we take in faith
the bread and wine. We give you thanks:
and praise your holy name.

Jesus, you will come to reign in glory. We
give you thanks:
**and praise your holy name.
Amen. Come, Lord Jesus!**

St Catharine's, Houghton on the Hill, Leicester

AT A CAROL SERVICE

CONFESSION

**Almighty God, our heavenly Father,
we have sinned against you,
through our own fault,
in thought and word and deed,
and in what we have left undone.
We are truly sorry
and repent of all our sins.
For your Son our Lord
    Jesus Christ's sake,
forgive us all that is past;
and grant that we may serve you
in newness of life
to the glory of your name. Amen.**

CREED

**I believe and trust in God the Father,
who made the world.**

**I believe and trust in his Son
    Jesus Christ,
who redeemed mankind.**

**I believe and trust in his Holy Spirit,
who gives life to the people of God.
Amen.**

OR

ACT OF FAITH (CREED)

Let us confess our faith in the Son of God:
**In the beginning was the Word,
and the Word was with God,
and the Word was God.
Through him all things were made;
without him nothing was made
    that has been made.
In him was life,
and that life was the light of us all.
The Word became flesh
and lived for a while among us;
we have seen his glory,
the glory of the one and only Son
who came from the Father,
full of grace and truth. Amen.** from John 1

THE LORD'S PRAYER

**Our Father in heaven,
hallowed be your name,
your kingdom come,
your will be done,
on earth as in heaven.
Give us today our daily bread.
Forgive us our sins
as we forgive those who sin against us.
Lead us not into temptation
but deliver us from evil.**

**For the kingdom, the power,
    and the glory are yours,
now and for ever. Amen.**

RESPONSES TO INTERCESSIONS

Lord, in your mercy,
hear our prayer.

FINAL RESPONSE

Merciful Father,
**accept these prayers
for the sake of your Son,
our Saviour Jesus Christ. Amen.**

THE GRACE

**The grace of our Lord Jesus Christ,
and the love of God,
and the fellowship of the Holy Spirit
be with us all evermore. Amen.**

OFFERTORY PRAYER

**Yours, Lord, is the greatness,
the power, the glory, the splendour,
and the majesty;
for everything in heaven and on earth
    is yours.
All things come from you,
and of your own do we give you.
Amen.**

CHRISTMAS PRAYERS

ACT OF PRAISE

Let us worship the Saviour:
Heavenly king, yet born of Mary; Jesus, Son of God,
we praise and adore you.
Eternal Word, yet child without speech; Jesus, Son of God,
we praise and adore you.
Robed in glory, yet wrapped in infant clothes; Jesus, Son of God,
we praise and adore you.
Lord of heaven and earth, yet laid in a manger; Jesus, Son of God,
we praise and adore you.

To you, O Jesus,
strong in your weakness,
glorious in your humility,
mighty to save,
be all praise and glory,
with the Father and the Holy Spirit,
now and for ever. Amen.

From 'Worship Now'
St Andrew's Press, Church of Scotland

CONFESSION

We confess that amid all the joys and festivities of this season we have sometimes forgotten what Christmas really means, and have left the Lord Jesus out of our thinking and living:
Father, forgive us.
Help us to remember that you loved the world so much that you gave your only Son, who was born to be our Saviour:
Lord, help us.
We confess that we have allowed the most important event in history to become dulled by familiarity:
Father, forgive us.
Help us in this act of worship to recapture a sense of wonder, and to discover again the stupendous fact that the Creator of the universe has come to us as a newborn baby:
Lord, help us.
We confess to a selfish enjoyment of Christmas while we do little to help the homeless families of your world:
Father, forgive us.

Fill our hearts with the love that cares,
that understands and gives;
show us how we can best serve
those in need;
for the sake of him
who was born in a stable,
Jesus Christ our Lord. Amen.

After John Searle, Jubilate Editors †

THANKSGIVING

God our Father, we listen again to the story of Christmas, and we are glad that Jesus has come to be our saviour and our friend.
We hear how Mary laid her baby in a manger. Jesus has come:
thank you, Father.
We hear how the angels sang over the Bethlehem hills: 'Glory to God; peace for the world.' Jesus has come:
thank you, Father.
We hear how the shepherds hurried to see that what the angel said was true. Jesus has come:
thank you, Father.
We hear how the wise men came to bring their worship and their precious gifts. Jesus has come:
thank you, Father.

O God, we thank you
that Jesus has come
to be our saviour and our friend:
we welcome him with love,
and worship him with gladness,
for your glory's sake. Amen.

From 'When You Pray With 7s – 10s'
© National Christian Education Council

BLESSING

The joy of the angels,
the wonder of the shepherds
and the peace of the Christ child,
fill *your* hearts this Christmas time;
and the blessing of God the Father,
God the Son, and God the Holy Spirit,
be with *you* now and always. **Amen.**

Michael Perry †

EPIPHANY PRAYERS

CONFESSION

Lord Jesus Christ, wise men from the East worshipped and adored you; they brought you gifts — gold, incense, and myrrh.

We too have seen your glory, but we have often turned away. Lord, in your mercy, **forgive us and help us.**

We too have gifts, but we have not fully used them or offered them to you. Lord, in your mercy, **forgive us and help us.**

We too have acclaimed you as King, but we have not served you with all our strength. Lord, in your mercy, **forgive us and help us.**

We too have acknowledged you as God, but we have not striven for holiness. Lord, in your mercy, **forgive us and help us.**

We too have welcomed you as Saviour, but we have failed to tell others of your love. Lord, in your mercy, **Forgive us and help us.**

Make our trust more certain,
make our love more true,
make our worship more acceptable;
for your glory's sake. Amen.

Michael Perry †

LITANY

Christ, born in a stable, give courage to all who are homeless; in your mercy, **hear our prayer.**

Christ, who fled into Egypt, give comfort to all refugees; in your mercy, **hear our prayer.**

Christ, who fasted in the desert, give relief to all who are hungry; in your mercy, **hear our prayer.**

Christ, who hung in torment on the cross, give your strength to all who suffer; in your mercy, **hear our prayer.**

Christ, who died to save us, give us the assurance of your forgiveness; in your mercy, **hear our prayer.**

Save us today,
and use us in your loving purposes;
for your glory's sake. Amen after Simon Baynes

Index